WELCOME

|||||||||||||||||||||||||||||||||||||||||||||||||||||||||||||||||||||||||||||||||||||||

Starting the keto diet can be a daunting change to your lifestyle, but worry not because Complete Keto Diet Book is here to help provide insight and know-how on all things keto. We'll cover the major benefits of the lifestyle, as well as explain what ketosis is and why it's so important. We'll also touch on keto flu and how you can alleviate some of its symptoms. Once you're armed with this new knowledge, it's time to delve into an array of delicious meals that you can cook for every occasion. From breakfasts and salads to weekend showstoppers and fakeaways, we're sure that you'll soon find a selection of favourite meals in no time. So what are you waiting for? It's time to take those bold first steps on your keto journey.

FUTURE

COMPLETE Keto DIET BOOK

Future PLC Quay House, The Ambury, Bath, BA1 1UA

Editorial
Editor **Drew Sleep**
Senior Designer **Lora Barnes**
Compiled by **Sarah Bankes & Briony Duguid**
Senior Art Editor **Andy Downes**
Head of Art & Design **Greg Whitaker**
Editorial Director **Jon White**

Contributors
Madelene King, Laurie Newman, Perry Wardell-Wicks

Photography
All copyrights and trademarks are recognised and respected

Advertising
Media packs are available on request
Commercial Director **Clare Dove**

International
Head of Print Licensing **Rachel Shaw**
licensing@futurenet.com
www.futurecontenthub.com

Circulation
Head of Newstrade **Tim Mathers**

Production
Head of Production **Mark Constance**
Production Project Manager **Matthew Eglinton**
Advertising Production Manager **Joanne Crosby**
Digital Editions Controller **Jason Hudson**
Production Managers **Keely Miller, Nola Cokely,
Vivienne Calvert, Fran Twentyman**

Printed by William Gibbons, 26 Planetary Road,
Willenhall, West Midlands, WV13 3XT

Distributed by Marketforce, 5 Churchill Place, Canary Wharf, London, E14 5HU
www.marketforce.co.uk Tel: 0203 787 9001

Complete Keto Diet Book Second Edition (LBZ4292)
© 2022 Future Publishing Limited

We are committed to only using magazine paper which is derived from responsibly managed,
certified forestry and chlorine-free manufacture. The paper in this bookazine was sourced
and produced from sustainable managed forests, conforming to strict environmental and
socioeconomic standards. The paper holds full FSC or PEFC certification and accreditation.

All contents © 2022 Future Publishing Limited or published under licence. All rights reserved.
No part of this magazine may be used, stored, transmitted or reproduced in any way without
the prior written permission of the publisher. Future Publishing Limited (company number
2008885) is registered in England and Wales. Registered office: Quay House, The Ambury,
Bath BA1 1UA. All information contained in this publication is for information only and is, as far
as we are aware, correct at the time of going to press. Future cannot accept any responsibility
for errors or inaccuracies in such information. You are advised to contact manufacturers and
retailers directly with regard to the price of products/services referred to in this publication. Apps
and websites mentioned in this publication are not under our control. We are not responsible for
their contents or any other changes or updates to them. This magazine is fully independent and
not affiliated in any way with the companies mentioned herein.

FUTURE

Connectors.
Creators.
Experience
Makers.

Future plc is a public
company quoted on the
London Stock Exchange
(symbol: FUTR)
www.futureplc.com

Chief executive **Zillah Byng-Thorne**
Non-executive chairman **Richard Huntingford**
Chief financial officer **Penny Ladkin-Brand**

Tel +44 (0)1225 442 244

**Widely
Recycled**

ipso. For press freedom
with responsibility

CONTENTS

RECIPES

{ FIND THE COVER RECIPE } on page 50

All About KETO

Discover what makes keto different to other diets and how it can help you to lose weight by eating and burning fat

The keto diet has been rising in popularity as a low-carbohydrate diet in recent years, thanks to a surge in celebrities adopting this regimen and its potential health benefits. Similar to the Atkins diet which drew attention in the early 2000s, keto focuses on restricting your carb intake while focusing on consuming a large amount of fat and protein. Though, unlike the Atkins diet, the keto diet doesn't ever allow you to gradually increase the amount of carbs you eat: once you cut them out, they're removed from the whole eating plan.

Over the next ten pages, we'll explore how the keto diet works, what ketosis is and the science behind how it can make the human body turn fat into fuel, how the diet can help epileptic patients relieve seizure symptoms, other health benefits and consider the potential risks. From there, we'll then examine the best foods to eat on a keto diet and which foods you should avoid. Finally, we'll look at how you can get started, how to stay keto as a home cook, tips for eating out at a restaurant and learn how to maintain the diet once you're underway. Let's get started with your keto journey!

Working out on the keto diet is an effective way to reduce your weight

5 BENEFITS OF KETO

BLOOD SUGAR CONTROL
Because of the restriction on foods in the keto diet, people with type 2 diabetes may find some benefit from a keto diet in controlling their blood sugar levels.

WEIGHT LOSS
By using fat as fuel, the body delves into unused fat stores, converting them into energy. As you shed pounds, you'll find it much easier to maintain and continue to lose weight.

BETTER FOCUS
The reduction in glucose in your body means you can improve focus and concentration. Ketones and fatty acids are a great source of fuel for the brain, too!

REDUCING HUNGER
People on low-carb ketogenic diets tend to feel less hungry. Ketosis reduces the levels of ghrelin, the 'hunger hormone' that creates the feeling of hunger pangs.

EPILEPSY
Developed as a treatment for epilepsy, studies have shown that a keto diet can reduce seizures in epileptic patients, as well as the number of medicines needed.

What is keto?

How does keto work and how does it make your body burn fat as fuel?

The keto, or 'ketogenic', diet is a high-fat and extremely low-carb diet that puts your body in a state called ketosis. After two-to-seven days, you'll gain access to fat stores you normally wouldn't be able to use for fuel, which is then burned to provide you with energy. The main component of a ketogenic diet is in consuming between 20g-50g of carbohydrates every day while focusing on high-fat and moderate-protein foods. That means no root vegetables, grains, some fruits and sugars, but yes to foods that fall under the leafy greens, high-fat dairy, meats and healthy oils categories. Typically, this diet would involve limiting your total daily calorific percentage of the three macronutrients (essential nutrients that help your body to function properly) to 55% to 60% for fat, 30% to 35% for protein and 5% to 10% for carbohydrates. It all sounds regimented and it's no surprise that keto diets have been rising in popularity in the last few years, but surprisingly, the diet's origins actually lie almost a century earlier in scientific research and as a treatment for epilepsy.

Various studies in the 1920s found that low-carb, high-fat diets could be used as a seizure treatment in patients with epilepsy. But, as medicine progressed through the years, the discovery of new anti-seizure medication eventually led to the decline of popularity in keto.

The diet fell out of fashion for decades, until it was thrust back into the spotlight in the 90s when Hollywood producer Jim Abrahams discussed using the keto diet to help treat his son's epilepsy on NBC's *Dateline*, rekindling scientific interest in the diet. Since then, there has been a widespread appeal in keto from a lifestyle perspective as it can help with losing weight, providing a steadier supply of energy and reducing hunger, among other benefits.

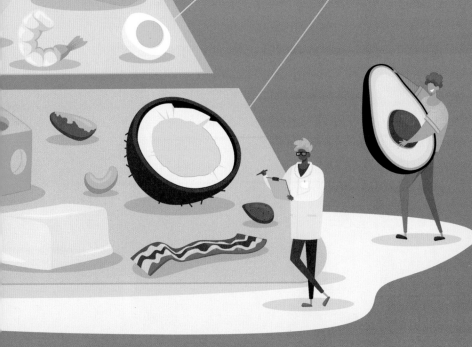

5-10% CARBS

30-35% PROTEIN

55-60% HEALTHY FATS

The science of ketosis

We've learned where the keto diet comes from, but how does it work in practice?

Our cells use up a lot of energy each day to keep our entire body running. Normally it fuels itself on glucose (in the form of glycogen), which we get by consuming carbs found in grains, vegetables and fruits. Glucose is the easiest type of energy for the body to absorb and is the preferred fuel source as it's the simplest form of sugar. As glucose is absorbed into our blood, insulin is produced, which helps the body to use up glucose for energy and provide an almost unlimited supply of fat that is stored for later.

But when the body has been starved of carbohydrates and therefore glucose, it runs off of the fatty acid ketone instead. Produced by the liver, these ketone bodies are made from our fat stores and power our muscles, creating energy to keep us going in the absence of glucose. This increased level of ketones in our system creates a metabolic state known as ketosis.

With a keto diet, you reduce your intake of carbs to 20g-50g a day so that your body will begin ketosis. This takes around two-to-seven days (though this rate can vary from person to person). Your cells' fuel supply will then switch to run on ketones instead of glucose and as you drop glucose levels, your insulin drops too. The loss of insulin levels dramatically increases fat burning, making it easier to lose weight. As you continue on with your keto diet, it will become easier to keep the weight off.

At the same time, you might notice a decrease in feelings of hunger while in ketosis. The increased level of ketones in your body suppresses ghrelin (the hormone that creates hunger pangs, stimulates appetite and promotes fat storage) helping you to control your weight loss programme further if that's your primary goal.

GLOSSARY

KETOSIS
The metabolic state the body goes into once it has been deprived of carbohydrates.

KETONES
When glucose levels drop, the liver converts fat into ketones to produce energy for the body.

GLUCOSE
Also known as blood sugar, glucose is converted into energy in our body and comes from the food we eat.

MACRONUTRIENTS
The nutrients we use in the largest amount. Carbohydrates, fat and protein are all examples of macronutrients.

INSULIN
A hormone made by the pancreas that helps the body to absorb glucose and regulate carbohydrates, fats and proteins.

How to achieve
Ketosis

Discover how you can quickly and methodically help your body reach a state of ketosis by following our step-by-step guide

Reaching ketosis is a crucial part of the keto diet and something that requires a bit of work on your part. It shouldn't be too difficult, though, and here we'll show you the steps you need to follow to take to achieve and maintain ketosis.

1. REDUCE CARBOHYDRATES
By removing your carbohydrate intake to 20g-50g a day, you will produce less glucose for the body to absorb and turn into energy. The depletion of glucose will make your liver create ketone bodies and start your journey towards ketosis.

2. STEP UP YOUR EXERCISE REGIME
When your glucose and glycogen levels are low, your liver will increase its production of ketones. Working out while already on a keto diet will boost the number of ketones in your body.

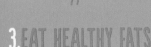

3. EAT HEALTHY FATS

At the same time, you should ensure you are eating good fats and proteins alongside a drastically reduced carbohydrate consumption. Healthy fats, such as avocado oil and fatty fish, are low in carbs and can increase ketone production.

4. EAT THE RIGHT LEVELS OF PROTEIN

Eating an excessive amount of protein can suppress ketosis, while undereating can lead to loss of muscle mass. Protein is needed for some areas of your body that ketones can't provide energy for as it is used to make glucose for red blood cells and so on.

5. TEST KETONE LEVELS

By making sure that each macronutrient is proportionally represented in your diet, you should be achieving ketosis quicker. Tests are available for urine, breath and blood, and these will indicate if you've reached ketosis, allowing you to adjust your routine and meals accordingly.

6. STAY ON THE DIET

By keeping to your meal plans, within two-to-seven days your liver will produce ketones that will start burning fat into energy and put your body into a state of ketosis.

Medical uses

More than just a method of losing weight, the keto diet has been explored as a potential treatment for other health conditions

The keto diet began life as a treatment for seizures, but over time other studies have shown its benefits for other health conditions. By reducing carbohydrate and glucose intake, a keto diet provides greater control over blood sugar and can help a type 2 diabetic with maintaining their glucose levels.

Improvements in cholesterol levels and blood pressures have led researchers to suggest that the keto diet can reduce the risk factors for heart disease. Similarly, because of the reduced production of insulin in the body, the keto diet could have a key role to play in polycystic ovary syndrome.

Finally, the keto diet is being explored as a treatment option for cancer as it could potentially slow tumour growth.

GOOD FOODS

NOW THAT WE KNOW THE SCIENCE OF KETO, WHICH FOODS ARE THE PERFECT FIT FOR THE DIET? **READ ON TO FIND OUT...**

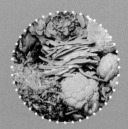

GREEN VEGGIES

Most green vegetables grown above ground are great for the keto diet. Leafy greens such as kale, spinach and lettuce will be your best bet for keeping carbohydrate consumption low. Other examples that have relatively low carb counts include avocados, Brussels sprouts, celery, courgettes (zucchini), asparagus, peppers, cucumbers, cabbage and cauliflower.

BERRIES

Small amounts of blackberries, blueberries strawberries and raspberries are okay for any sweet tooth. Other fruits contain more natural sugars and therefore more carbohydrates. It may seem weird to cut out so much fruit, but we can actually get more vitamins and nutrients from veggies. For example, there is more vitamin C in peppers and kale than in an orange!

NUTS

Pecans, Brazils and macadamias are worth getting nutty about as they all contain 5g or less of carbohydrates per 100g while being rich in other useful macronutrients. Other nuts such as hazelnuts, walnuts, peanuts, almonds and pine nuts provide 10g and under per 100g, which works out at a few handfuls depending on the size of the nut.

EGGS AND MEATS

With zero carbohydrates per 100g, eggs and most meats are incredibly keto-friendly foods and should be a cornerstone of your ketogenic diet. Beef, lamb, chicken and pork are all great sources of proteins - but do be careful of bacon that's been cured with sugar. Processed meats, sausages and meatballs may also contain added carbs, so always check the label.

FOODS TO AVOID

A KETO DIET IS NOT AS SIMPLE AS ONLY EATING FRUITS AND VEGETABLES, AS SOME FRESH PRODUCE ARE NATURALLY HIGHER IN CARBS

GRAINS

Cereals, bread, pasta, rice and any food made from a grain are not beneficial for a keto diet as they are very high in carbohydrates and are very starchy. Beer surprisingly falls into this category too as it is brewed from cereal grains, though keto versions are available.

ROOT VEGETABLES AND TUBERS

If it's a vegetable that grows below ground, then the general rule of thumb is to avoid it in the keto diet. So this means no potatoes, sweet potatoes, carrots, parsnips and so on. Again, these vegetables are very starchy and very high in carbohydrates.

MOST FRUITS

Did you know that just one banana provides you with enough carbohydrates for your daily keto limit? Other fruits contain a lot of natural sugar, which should be avoided in the keto diet. However, a small handful of berries are typically okay if moderated with the rest of your meal plan.

SUGARY FOOD & DRINKS

You'll have to forego your favourite chocolate, cakes and soda in the keto diet to stay on track. As they are intensely sweet and full of sugar, they should be best avoided. Although diet sodas don't contain any sugar, they should be avoided too as they maintain your sweet cravings.

SEAFOOD

Not only are fish and shellfish naturally nutritious and full of good fatty omega-3 acids that boost brain and heart health, they also tend to have an abundance of vitamin B12 and iodine too. Salmon and trout have zero carbohydrates, while other seafood such as mussels, clams, squid, octopus and oysters all have under 5g of carbohydrates per 100g.

DAIRY (BUT NOT MILK)

Heavy cream, butter, Greek yoghurt and cheese are all generally high in fat and protein, but low in carbohydrates. Though you should keep in mind that not all dairy products are equally high in fat. If the milk produce has been fermented with bacteria, then it will be lower in carbohydrates as lactose (the sugar) will have been fermented into lactic acids.

OILS AND SAUCES

Any oils with thousands of years of history and minimal processing (such as pure olive oil, coconut oil, avocado oil, sesame oil and so on) are great for ketogenic diets. Most sauces are okay, too, as long as they're not sugary, for example mustard, vinaigrette (made without any sweet ingredients), Hollandaise, aioli, salsa, soy sauce, guacamole and pesto.

DRINKS

Water is essential no matter what diet you're on as it naturally hydrates our bodies. Unsweetened coffee and tea with heavy cream instead of milk is a great choice if you need a morning caffeine boost, too. Other diets may restrict alcohol consumption, but dry white and red wine don't have that many carbohydrates in and can be drunk in a keto diet in moderation.

MILK

Though not seemingly sweet, milk has about 15g of carbohydrates in a single glass. That means adding a splash into your hot drinks can quickly add up, especially in a heavily milk-based pick-me-up like a latte. Consider using heavy cream instead if you need a creamy taste in your coffee or tea.

'LIGHT' FOODS

Always check the label of what you're buying as some foods marketed as 'light', such as light yoghurts for example, contain the same amount of sugar as a non-light version. Sometimes the amount of sugar could be almost as high as a fruity yoghurt - and we know we should avoid most fruits in the keto diet.

SWEET CONDIMENTS & PROCESSED OILS

Some condiments such as ketchup, BBQ sauce, jams and chutneys contain a very high level of sugars. Jam contains as much as 69g of carbohydrates per 100g, for example! Vegetable oil and sunflower oil are not recommended for a keto diet either, as are any processed foods cooking using these oils.

LEGUMES

Beans and chickpeas all fall under the legume category and are fairly high in carbohydrates, so those on keto diets should avoid eating large quantities of them. They do provide some good nutrients such as iron, however, so a small amount might be okay depending on the rest of the foods that you have consumed on the day.

Knowing the risks

There are some potentially negative long-term effects, as well as groups of people that shouldn't start the keto diet at all...

The keto diet is safe for most but those that are pregnant and or breastfeeding, and people with high blood pressure, should all take extra care and consult a doctor before starting the keto diet. Always seek medical advice from a professional.

For anyone with high blood pressure, you should be mindful that the general advice of consuming more salt and water in the form of bouillon or broth in the first week of the diet may not be the best treatment for dehydration as it will increase blood pressure. Also, if you're also already on blood pressure medication while starting the keto diet, there's the chance that the diet will lower your blood pressure to a level that may make you feel dizzy and weak, in which case you should contact your doctor to discuss if the medication

you are currently taking is right for you while on the diet.

Anyone breastfeeding should not be on a low-carb diet at all. Breastfeeding on a low-carb intake can lead to ketoacidosis, which can be life-threatening. It should be noted that ketoacidosis is not the same as ketosis, and is where blood acidity is increased.

Additionally, getting the body to change its energy source to run on fats may not be safe for those who are pregnant. A study of pregnant mice on a keto diet found that the offspring had slower growth, organ dysfunctions, smaller hearts and brains as well as enlarged spines. There haven't been any studies on pregnant humans, understandably, to see if these effects are the same for our species. The keto diet has also been associated with causing dysmenorrhea, or painful period cramps too.

While the ketogenic diet is helpful for diabetics to control their blood sugar, without careful administration they could also suffer from severe hypoglycaemia. Any diabetics with type 2 diabetes and using sodium-glucose cotransporter 2 (SGLT2) inhibitors should also avoid the diet.

You should also be wary that a high-fat, high-protein diet can cause problems in people with existing liver and kidney conditions. As the keto diet can put extra stress on the kidney, it could also lead to the formation of kidney stones.

A high level of red meat consumption may also increase the risk of cancer. And though you can eat steak, bacon and butter on the diet, regular consumption could lead to an increased risk for heart disease and high cholesterol without the guidance of a doctor.

" IF YOU ARE CONCERNED, TAKE EXTRA CARE AND CONSULT A DOCTOR BEFORE STARTING THE KETO DIET "

IRRITABILITY?

DEHYDRATION?

HEADACHE?

What are the side effects?

Both positive and negative changes to your body will happen in the first few days of starting the keto diet

As the body has to switch its metabolic state into ketosis, there can be some short-term side effects while it gets used to using fat as fuel. Some of these symptoms can include headache, tiredness, difficulty focusing, lack of motivation, irritability, sugar cravings, cramping, general weakness, dehydration, excess urination, muscle fatigue, diarrhoea, discomfort, dizziness and heart palpitations.

Known as the 'keto flu', these effects are caused by loss of water retention from a carb-filled diet. Because the levels of carbohydrates and insulin have drastically dropped, the body excretes more sodium and water in urine – causing dehydration and some of the other effects.

Some other symptoms include bad (or fruity) breath, which is also an indication that your body is in ketosis. This is because a ketone body, acetone, is trying to escape via your exhalations and may make your breath smell fruity or similar to the smell of nail polish remover. This smell can also be present in sweat if someone is working out in the first few days of the keto diet.

These side effects will dissipate after a few days, and up to a week or so of starting the diet. On the positive side, as water retention is lost, you will drastically lose weight in the early stages of being on the keto diet, which is a somewhat beneficial side effect for those with weight-loss goals. Some people also experience reduced hunger pangs and an increase of energy once they are able to focus again as the negative keto flu symptoms disappear.

TIREDNESS ?

KETO FLU?

HOW TO MINIMISE SIDE EFFECTS

There are several ways to reduce the negative effects that come from the first week of a keto diet

Everyone is affected differently by ketosis. Some experience more intense effects, while others may feel hardly any differences at all. There are different methods that can decrease symptoms if you do find yourself experiencing them.

Rather than cutting carbs cold turkey, you could gradually reduce carbohydrate intake to 20g-50g over several weeks to help the body get more used to the change, though this would also mean slower progress.

An increased consumption of salts and water will help too, and drinking a cup or two of broth or bouillon is a great method for immediately alleviating headache, nausea and dizziness symptoms. As a rule of thumb, drinking more water will also relieve symptoms. This can be a combination of water, broth, coffee and teas but do be careful with caffeinated drinks, as they can dehydrate you if you consume too many cups and will reverse the hard work you've put into alleviating symptoms.

Increasing your fat intake in the first week will make the body feel satiated for longer, too, while you reduce carbs and will make you feel less hungry after a meal.

Once the side effects settle down, you can look at decreasing fat back to 55%-65% of your calorific total daily.

If you do find yourself unable to function properly for a couple of days, it may make sense to reduce your exercise routine or even stop it completely while your body properly adjusts to burning fat for fuel.

Getting started

Now that we know what makes a good keto ingredient, where do we begin with the diet?

HOME MEALS

The best way to get started is to create a meal plan for a week. Having a routine in place helps you to stick to the diet, and avoid going off course. Design each meal around keto-friendly foods and avoiding heavily processed foods (which tend to be carb-heavy anyway), so that you are eating nutritious foods and are fully prepared when it comes to mealtime. This will keep you on track and also help you with your grocery shopping too.

Learn some easy midweek staple keto meals that will keep you going and know the ingredients that go into them inside and out. It might even help to create some keto versions of

Starting a diet plan or recipe book can help you with planning meals ahead of time

your favourite foods, like courgetti and meatballs instead of spaghetti and meatballs.

You can adapt as you go, too, adding in new recipes and bringing back old favourites along the way to keep your weekly meal plans interesting.

EATING OUT

Heading out for dinner doesn't have to be a chore on a keto diet, though planning ahead will save any headaches at the restaurant. Most places will have their menus available to view online nowadays, so you can have a look ahead of time to find keto-friendly options in advance. A lot of restaurants will be happy to customise your order, too, should you not find any suitable default menu options. For side orders, consider substituting carbohydrates like fries with a side salad. If the eatery doesn't allow substitutions, simply ask for the starchy carbohydrate to be removed, for example when ordering a burger you can ask for it to arrive without the bun. If you are really stuck for main options, try to use a combination of side dishes to your advantage.

Just remember to avoid dessert and to be careful of sugary drinks like sweet wines and sodas, and avoid condiments like ketchup and BBQ sauce.

A simple substitution can turn a carb-heavy meal into a keto-friendly alternative

Keeping

There are a lot of things you can do to maintain your keto diet no matter what life throws at you

You're well underway and a few weeks along into a ketogenic diet, so now what? The best thing you can do is to keep meal planning and stick to it, ensuring that the only foods within your grasp are all keto-friendly so you are never tempted to stray off course. You can do this by either throwing or giving away all of your carby foods, or by putting them in hard-to-reach places.

Beating your cravings may be hard – especially if you have a sweet tooth. But you can keep those cravings at bay by making keto-friendly versions of the food you love, or by delaying your craving with a keto meal first to keep you satisfied.

Eating a keto snack ahead of a social event can remove the temptation to pick at carby foods

t up!

It can also be tough being keto while managing life and social events where you'll ultimately be faced with food and drink-related challenges. If you go to a friend's or family member's home for dinner, it might be wise to communicate ahead of time so the host can prepare options for you. It may even make sense to have a high-fat snack that will keep you full before you leave so that you will be less tempted by carby entrees. However, it is ultimately down to how strict your meal plans are, and if you're happy with being a bit loose with your intake while you're out.

Finally, why not join a keto community on social media? Keto groups are great for recipe inspiration and connecting with like-minded people, keeping you motivated to carry on with your diet.

5 RULES OF Keto

- 5-10% Carbs
- 30-35% Protein
- 50-60% Healthy Fats

1 STICK TO THE RIGHT AMOUNTS

Keep your carb intake to between 20g-50g, and your calorific breakdown equates to 55% to 60% for fat, 30% to 35% for protein and 5% to 10% carbohydrates.

2 EAT THE RIGHT FOODS

High fat and protein are allowed, while anything carby, starchy, with a lot of sugar or grains should be avoided.

3 PLAN YOUR MEALS

Maintain your diet by planning a grocery list of keto-friendly foods and organise your meals ahead of time.

4 DRINK WATER

Staying hydrated is essential for the first week of the keto diet, but is generally a good rule of thumb to live by no matter the diet.

5 PREPARE FOR KETO FLU

By making sure you have ways of alleviating the side effects from keto flu, you'll achieve ketosis easier and happier.

Masala Omelette

An omelette makes a quick and easy, super-healthy meal. We've used Indian flavours here to spice up this veggie staple

Serves 2 • Ready in 30 mins

INGREDIENTS

- 2 eggs plus 3 whites
- handful of spinach
- 6 cherry tomatoes, halved
- ½ small green chilli
- ½tbsp garam masala
- ½tsp turmeric
- ½tsp cumin
- 1tsp olive oil
- ½ red onion, sliced
- 2 spring onions, chopped
- ½ bunch coriander, optional

METHOD

1 Beat the eggs and whites, and season them. Mix in the spinach, halve the tomatoes, the chilli and spices, reserving a little chilli.

2 Heat the oil in a small frying pan over a medium heat, and fry the red onion and most of the spring onions until softened. Pour in the egg mix and swirl around the pan so the eggs cook evenly, then leave until almost set. Fold in half so the outside sets and the middle is soft.

3 Top with the remaining tomatoes, the extra chilli and spring onion (and the coriander, if using), to serve.

INFORMATION
Per Serving

CALORIES
123

FAT
7g

SATURATED FAT
2g

CARBS
1.5g

RECIPES AND STYLING: JESSICA FINDLAY. PHOTOGRAPHY: SEAN CALITZ. PROP STYLING: SUE ROWLANDS

One-pan Breakfast Fry

*Not one to be eaten every day but this decadent day-starter
is great as a special treat!*

Serves 4 • Ready in 25 mins

INGREDIENTS

- 1tbsp olive oil
- 4 sausages
- 1 pepper, sliced
- 70g | 2½oz bacon lardons
- 150g | 5¼oz mushrooms, sliced
- ½tsp paprika
- 2 tomatoes, halved
- 4 eggs
- 75g | 2¾oz cheddar, grated

METHOD

1 Heat the oil in a large frying pan, add the sausages and fry for five minutes. Add the pepper and lardons, and fry for a further ten minutes until golden. Remove the sausages, slice and return to the pan with the mushrooms and paprika, and fry for five minutes. Add the tomatoes

2 Heat the grill to medium. Crack the eggs into the pan and cook for a few minutes until the white has almost set.

3 Scatter over the cheese and grill for three to four minutes until it's bubbling and the eggs are cooked.

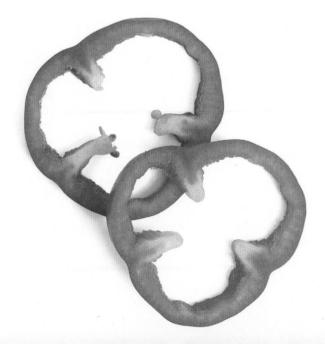

INFORMATION
Per Serving

CALORIES
400

FAT
31g

SATURATED FAT
11.5g

CARBS
7g

Avocado, Bacon, Pecan and Chicory Salad

We love this salad as a lunch but it works perfectly for dinner, too

Serves 4 • Ready in 15 mins

INGREDIENTS

FOR THE SALAD

- 200g | 7oz smoked streaky bacon or pancetta, thinly sliced and cut in half
- 2 heads of chicory, leaves separated
- 3 avocados, halved and sliced
- 50g | 1¾oz pecan nuts, thinly sliced

FOR THE DRESSING

- 5tbsp avocado oil
- 1tbsp white wine vinegar
- 1 shallot, finely sliced
- 2tsp wholegrain mustard

METHOD

1 In two batches, dry-fry the streaky bacon or pancetta in a pan until crisp.

2 Put all the chicory leaves in a salad bowl, then top with the avocado, bacon or pancetta, and pecans.

3 For the dressing, whisk together all the ingredients in a small bowl with 1tbsp water. Season to taste. Spoon over the salad just before serving.

INFORMATION
Per Serving

CALORIES
600

FAT
57g

SATURATED FAT
11g

CARBS
7g

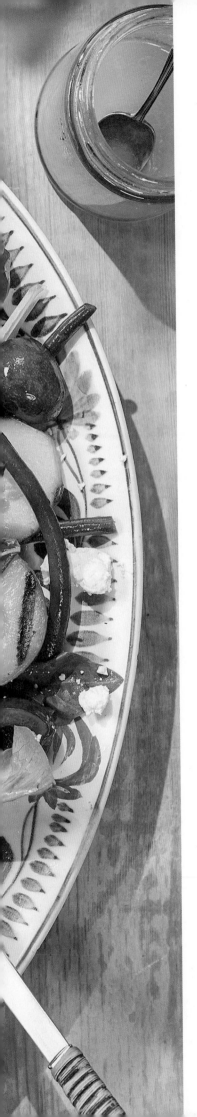

Fruity Feta and Green Bean Salad

Think of this salad as a savoury fruit bowl. Grilling summer fruits makes them a perfect match for salty cheeses

Serves 6 • Ready in 20 mins

INGREDIENTS

FOR THE SALAD

- 150g | 5¼oz green beans
- 2 peaches
- 2 nectarines
- 10 cherries
- 1tbsp olive oil, in a small bowl
- 1 little gem or romaine lettuce
- ½ cucumber, cut into rounds
- 1 large tomato
- 150g | 5¼oz feta

FOR THE VINAIGRETTE

- juice of 1 lemon
- 6 tbsp extra-virgin olive oil
- ½ tsp yellow mustard

METHOD

1 Bring a pan of water to the boil and blanch the beans for around six minutes, until al dente. Drain and plunge into iced water. When cool, drain.

2 For the vinaigrette, mix the lemon, oil and mustard with a pinch of salt and pepper in a lidded jar. Shake well and set aside.

3 Halve and stone the fruits, then pat or brush all over with the oil. Grill or griddle on medium-high for four minutes on each side, then set aside to cool in the fridge.

4 Rinse and dry the lettuce leaves, then mix them in a large bowl with the cucumber and tomato. Add the chargrilled fruits, give the vinaigrette another shake and add this too, until everything is well-coated. Serve on a large summer platter with the feta crumbled on top.

INFORMATION
Per Serving

CALORIES
280

FAT
11g

SATURATED FAT
4.2g

CARBS
9g

Green Goodness Soup

A revitalising bowl of joy – just what the doctor ordered!

Serves 4 • Ready in 30 mins

INGREDIENTS

- ½tbsp olive oil
- 1 bunch spring onions, chopped
- 6 anchovies, chopped
- 2 garlic cloves, chopped
- 1l | 2pts vegetable stock
- 200ml | 6¾fl oz coconut milk
- 1 head broccoli, broken into florets
- 100g | 3½oz frozen peas
- 2tbsp pumpkin or sunflower seeds
- 1tsp tamari
- 250g | 8¾oz spinach
- 1 small bunch each tarragon, basil, mint and parsley (reserve a little to serve)
- juice of ½ lemon

METHOD

1 Heat the oil in a large pan and fry the spring onions, anchovies and garlic for a few minutes. Add the stock and coconut milk (reserving a little to serve), and simmer for a few minutes before adding the broccoli, then simmer for five minutes. Add the peas and cook for a minute, then remove from the heat.

2 To make the toasted seeds, toss the seeds with the tamari in a frying pan over a medium heat for a few minutes, ensuring they don't burn. Set aside.

3 Stir the spinach through the soup until just wilted, then add the herbs and blend the soup with a stick blender until smooth. Stir through the lemon juice and top with a little coconut milk, the reserved herbs and toasted seeds to serve.

INFORMATION
Per Serving

CALORIES
224

FAT
15g

SATURATED FAT
15g

CARBS
9g

27

Green Beans and Burrata

Burrata is a fresh Italian cheese made with buffalo mozzarella and fresh cream – wonderfully indulgent!

Serves 4 • Ready in 15 mins

INGREDIENTS

- 250g | 8¾oz green beans, trimmed
- 150g | 5¼oz cherry tomatoes
- 4tbsp extra virgin olive oil, plus extra to drizzle
- juice of 1 large lemon
- 50g | 1¾oz toasted hazelnuts, chopped
- 2 balls burrata

METHOD

1 Blanch the beans in boiling water then refresh under cold water and drain. Halve or quarter the tomatoes. Whisk the oil with the lemon juice, and season well. Toss the beans and tomatoes in the dressing. Put onto a serving plate.

2 Scatter over the hazelnuts and split each burrata into two. Grind over some black pepper and add a little extra oil.

INFORMATION
Per Serving

CALORIES
400

FAT
35g

SATURATED FAT
11g

CARBS
4g

Squid Salad with Garlic and Chilli

Master the simple art of cooking squid and this would make a tasty lunch or starter

Serves 4 • Ready in 20 mins

INGREDIENTS

- 800g | 1lb 12¼oz squid, cut into large pieces
- 5tbsp olive oil
- 4 fat red chillies, sliced
- 6 garlic cloves, sliced
- 2tbsp sunflower oil
- 150g | 5¼oz rocket
- juice of 2 lemons

METHOD

1 Toss the squid in 2tbsp olive oil with plenty of black pepper. Set aside or you can leave it to marinate overnight in the fridge. Shallow-fry the chillies and garlic in the sunflower oil until just crispy. Drain on kitchen paper.

2 Grill the squid on a barbecue until charred on both sides. It literally takes a few minutes. Put into a bowl with the remaining olive oil. Toss in the rocket, lemon juice and the chillies and garlic with plenty of sea salt, and serve.

INFORMATION
Per Serving

CALORIES
335

FAT
23g

SATURATED FAT
4g

CARBS
0g

Steak and Blue Cheese Salad with a Walnut Pesto Dressing

There's nothing quite like a good steak. We've ditched the chips in favour of salad here for a lighter, keto-friendly option. If you have the time, and the willpower, this is delicious made with barbecued steak

Serves 2 • Ready in 30 mins

INGREDIENTS

FOR THE SALAD
- 250g | 8¾oz sirloin steak
- 2tsp olive oil
- 100g | 5½oz cherry tomatoes, roughly chopped
- 50g | 1¾oz watercress
- 50g | 1¾oz blue cheese

FOR THE PESTO
- 1 bunch of basil
- 1 garlic clove
- 75g | 2¾oz walnuts
- 30g | 1oz Parmesan
- 150ml | 5fl oz olive oil

METHOD

1 Allow the steak to reach room temperature. Rub well with the olive oil, and season generously. Bring a heavy-bottomed frying pan to a medium-high heat and cook the steak for three to four minutes on each side. Remove from the heat and rest.

2 To make the pesto, add all the ingredients to a food processor and blitz until smooth. Toss the cherry tomatoes in 1tbsp of pesto to dress.

3 Slice the steak thickly and arrange on plates with the tomatoes, watercress and crumbled blue cheese. Serve with some more pesto on the side.

INFORMATION
Per Serving

CALORIES
392

FAT
26g

SATURATED FAT
9g

CARBS
3g

Warm Salad of Jerusalem Artichokes

Drop the peeled artichokes wedges into a bowl of cold water with a few slices of lemon to prevent them blackening

Serves 6 • Ready in 40 mins

INGREDIENTS

FOR THE SALAD

- 500g | 1lb 1½oz Jerusalem artichokes, peeled and cut into wedges
- 2tbsp olive oil
- 40g | 1½oz butter
- handful of sage leaves
- 500g | 1lb 1½oz mixed wild mushrooms, cleaned and sliced
- ½ garlic clove, crushed
- 150g | 5¼oz baby spinach leaves

FOR THE DRESSING:

- 1 egg yolk
- ½ garlic clove, crushed
- juice of 1 small lemon
- 100ml | 3½fl oz olive oil

METHOD

1 Heat the oven to 200C | Gas 6 | 400F. Steam the artichoke wedges for ten minutes. Transfer to a roasting tin, toss with oil and season. Roast for 30 minutes.

2 For the dressing, whisk together the egg yolk, garlic, a pinch of salt and 2tsp lemon juice in a bowl. Whisking continuously, add the oil, drop by drop, until the mixture begins to thicken, then add the rest in a thin stream. Whisk in the remaining lemon juice and 2-3tbsp water to thin the consistency slightly.

3 Heat 10g | ¼oz butter in a frying pan and add the sage. Cook for a minute until translucent, not browned, then drain on kitchen paper to crisp as they cool.

4 Heat the remaining butter until it foams, then add the mushrooms and season well. Add the garlic and cook over a high heat for four to five minutes, until golden in places. Add the artichoke wedges and toss to combine. Spoon onto serving plates with the spinach leaves, scatter with sage leaves and spoon over plenty of dressing.

INFORMATION
Per Serving

CALORIES
268

FAT
23g

SATURATED FAT
5g

CARBS
9g

35

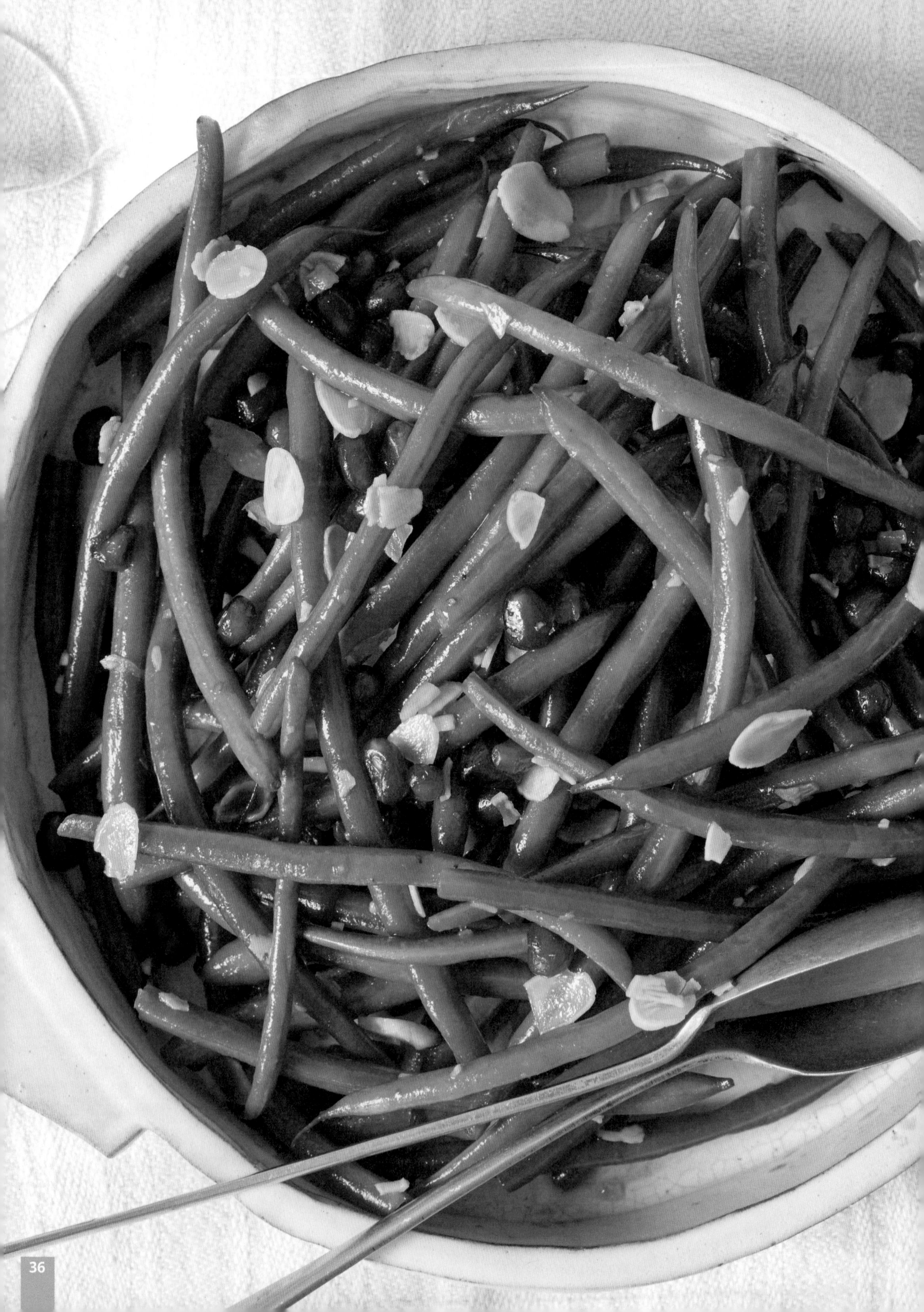

Green Beans with Toasted Almonds and Pomegranates

This dish makes for a fresh and tasty accompaniment for a special roast dinner

Serves 6 • Ready in 10 mins

INGREDIENTS

- 600g | 1lb 5oz green beans
- 1tbsp lemon juice
- 3tbsp olive oil
- 2tbsp pomegranate molasses
- 2tsp keto maple syrup
- 60g | 2oz pomegranate seeds
- 30g | 1oz flaked almonds, toasted

METHOD

1 Blanch the beans in a pan of water. Stir together the lemon juice, oil, molasses and syrup, and toss in the beans.

2 Sprinkle with the pomegranate seeds and almonds.

INFORMATION
Per Serving

CALORIES
41

FAT
2g

SATURATED FAT
0.1g

CARBS
4g

37

INFORMATION
Per Serving

CALORIES
675

FAT
49g

SATURATED FAT
17g

CARBS
12.5g

TIP
Wooden skewers can burn easily, even if well-soaked, so it's worth buying metal ones

Pork Satay with Peanut Sauce

The marinade and the sauce follow the same recipe with a couple of extra additions so it's hassle-free. You can use the same recipe for beef or chicken, too

Serves 4 • Ready in 30 mins, plus marinating

INGREDIENTS

FOR THE SKEWERS

- 450g | 1lb free-range pork fillet
- 100g | 3½oz salted peanuts, finely chopped

FOR THE MARINADE

- a large bunch of coriander
- zest and juice of 3 limes
- 1tbsp Thai fish sauce
- 175g | 6¼oz smooth peanut butter
- 200ml | 6¾fl oz coconut milk
- 1 lemongrass stalk, bashed and roughly chopped
- 1 red chilli

METHOD

1 To prepare the marinade, put the coriander stalks (keep the leaves for later) with all the marinade ingredients into a blender and whizz up until smooth.

2 Cut the pork into cubes and thread onto skewers. Use half the marinade to coat the pork and leave, covered, in the fridge to marinate for four hours or overnight.

3 Make the sauce with the remaining marinade, adding coriander leaves and the chopped peanuts. Grill the pork skewers until cooked through. Serve with the sauce.

King Prawns with Thai Dipping Sauce

This is simple finger food at its best – just peel and dip!

Serves 6 • Ready in 15 mins

INGREDIENTS

- 3 garlic cloves, crushed
- 3cm | 1in piece fresh ginger, grated
- 1 lemongrass stalk, finely chopped
- 1 red chilli, finely chopped
- 2tbsp rice wine vinegar
- 2tbsp soy sauce
- 1tsp sesame oil
- large handful of fresh coriander leaves, chopped
- 24 large raw king prawns, shell on
- 1tbsp olive oil
- salt flakes and lime wedges

METHOD

1 In a small bowl, mix together the garlic, ginger, lemongrass, chilli, rice wine vinegar, soy sauce, sesame oil and coriander. Stir in 2tbsp water and set aside.

2 Toss the prawns in the olive oil and cook on a barbecue heated to high for three minutes, turning occasionally, until pink and cooked through. Sprinkle with salt and serve with lime wedges and the sauce.

TIP

For a cheat sauce, mix 1tbsp red curry paste with 2tbsp rice wine vinegar, 2tbsp soy sauce and 2tbsp water

INFORMATION
Per Serving

CALORIES
81

FAT
3g

SATURATED FAT
0.5g

CARBS
3g

Spiced Lamb and Peri-peri Chicken Skewers

This lamb dish is ideal for hot summer evenings with friends and family

Serves 8 • Ready in 30 mins, plus marinating

INGREDIENTS

FOR THE LAMB

- 5tbsp olive oil
- 5tbsp red wine vinegar
- 2tbsp Brazilian barbecue marinade mix
- 1tbsp thyme leaves
- zest and juice of 1 lime, plus 1 lime cut into 8 wedges
- 2 garlic cloves, crushed
- 1kg | 2lb 3¼oz lamb leg steaks, cubed

FOR THE CHICKEN

- 25g | ¾oz packet peri-peri rub
- 4tbsp olive oil
- zest and juice of 1 lemon
- 2tsp thyme leaves
- 1 red onion, cut into wedges
- a few bay leaves
- 600g | 1lb 5oz chicken breast fillets
- 8 mild Peppadew peppers
- a few thyme sprigs and red pepper dip

METHOD

1 For the lamb, mix together the oil, red wine vinegar, marinade, thyme, lime zest and juice, and garlic. Add the lamb, stir, cover and chill for a few hours.

2 For the chicken, mix the peri-peri rub, oil, lemon zest and juice, thyme, onion and bay leaves. Add the chicken, stir, cover and chill for a few hours.

3 Heat the barbecue to high. Thread the meat onto skewers adding lime to the lamb, and onion and peppers to the chicken. Grill for 15 to 20 minutes. Scatter with thyme and serve with the dip.

INFORMATION
Per Serving

CALORIES
400

FAT
23g

SATURATED FAT
6g

CARBS
3g

Bourbon-glazed Beef Short Ribs

Marinate these overnight if you can for increased flavour

Serves 8 • Ready in 3 hours and 30 minutes

INGREDIENTS

FOR THE RIBS

- 2 racks of beef short ribs, about 2½kg/5½lbs
- 2tsp smoked paprika
- 2tbsp bourbon or whisky
- 2tbsp keto maple syrup
- 1l | 2pt rich beef stock

FOR THE GLAZE

- 2tbsp concentrated beef stock
- 2tbsp keto maple syrup
- 1tbsp bourbon or whisky

TIP

Your butcher can prepare the ribs by splitting racks into separate ribs and cutting in half for a perfect size

METHOD

1 Toss the ribs in the paprika, bourbon and syrup. Add black pepper. If you can, marinate the ribs overnight in a sealed plastic bag in the fridge. When you're ready to cook them, allow them to get back to room temperature.

2 To cook, heat the oven to 150C | Gas 2 | 300F. Put the ribs and any marinade in one or two roasting tins – you don't want them overcrowded. Add the stock, cover with foil and leave to cook slowly in the oven for three hours.

3 Then, to barbecue, take the ribs out of their cooking liquid. Mix together the glaze ingredients. You want the barbecue on a medium heat. Put the ribs on the grill and, brushing frequently with the glaze, cook for about 20 minutes or until brown and sticky.

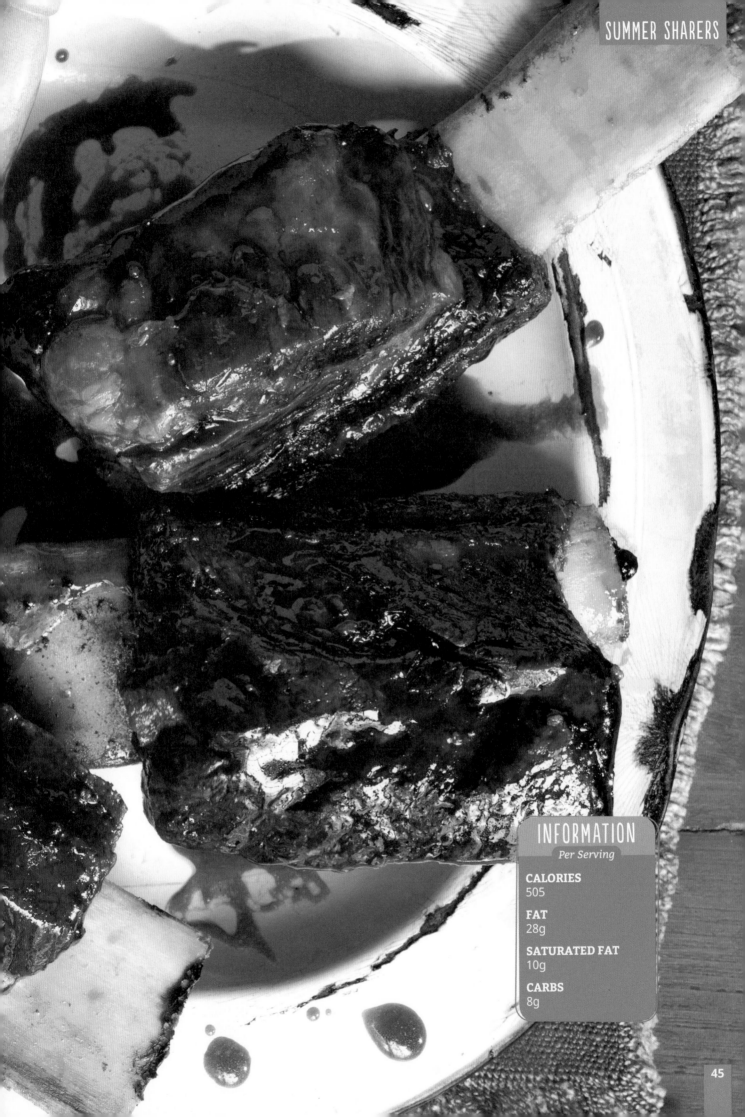

INFORMATION
Per Serving

CALORIES
505

FAT
28g

SATURATED FAT
10g

CARBS
8g

RECIPE AND FOOD STYLING: ELISA ROCHE, ROSE FOOKS, KEIRON GEORGE AND ROSIE BENSBERG. PHOTOS: SEAN CALITZ. PROPS: SUE ROWLANDS

INFORMATION
Per Serving

CALORIES
289

FAT
13g

SATURATED FAT
5.6g

CARBS
9.2g

Chicken Kebabs with Feta Salad

This light summery dish is perfect for warm evenings

Serves 2 • Ready in 25 minutes, plus marinating

INGREDIENTS

- 2 chicken breasts, roughly cubed
- ½tsp oregano
- ½tsp paprika
- 2 garlic cloves, sliced
- zest and juice of 1 lemon
- 1 red pepper, sliced
- 1tbsp olive oil
- 250g | 8¾oz yoghurt
- 50g | 1¾oz rocket
- 1 avocado, sliced
- 200g | 7oz feta, crumbled
- ½ cucumber

METHOD

1 Mix the chicken in the oregano, paprika, garlic, and lemon zest and juice. Leave to marinate for two hours, or overnight.

2 Bring the chicken to room temperature. Roast or grill the pepper slices with a drizzle of oil plus seasoning, until lightly blackened. Set aside.

3 Thread the chicken onto skewers. Place under a hot grill or cook on a hot griddle for ten minutes, turning throughout.

4 Serve with the roasted pepper, yogurt, rocket, avocado, feta and cucumber.

Salmon en Papillote with Fennel, Lemons and Pernod

Cooking 'en papillote' or 'in paper' is perfect for summer barbecues, as all the ingredients cook together

Serves 6 • Ready in 40 minutes

INGREDIENTS

- 2 bulbs of fennel (core removed), sliced (save the fronds for garnish)
- 4 echalion shallots, peeled and halved
- 40g | 1½oz butter, diced
- 50ml | 1¾fl oz Pernod
- 20ml | ¾fl oz white wine
- ½ bunch fresh parsley, chopped
- 500g | 1lb 1½oz skin-on side of salmon
- 1 red grapefruit, cut into segments

METHOD

1 Blanch the fennel in a pan of salted water. Drain and plunge into iced water.

2 Fold a sheet of baking paper in half along the width, open back up and arrange the fennel and shallots on one side, leaving at least 5cm | 2in around the edges. Dot cubes of butter over the vegetables, pour over the alcohol and scatter with half the parsley. Place the salmon on top and season.

3 Fold over the baking paper, and fold and twist the edges from one side to the other. Place on a barbecue and cook for 25 minutes.

4 Transfer to a large plate or board, rip open the paper and scatter over the grapefruit, along with the remaining parsley. Garnish with fennel fronds.

INFORMATION
Per Serving

CALORIES
470

FAT
21g

SATURATED FAT
3.3g

CARBS
4.8g

Beer-cured Pork

Curing meat in a wet brine makes it tender and won't dry out when cooked

Serves 6 • Ready in 20 minutes, plus marinating

INGREDIENTS

- 6 pork loin chops
- 500ml | 1pt low-carb beer
- 85g | 3oz ground sea salt
- a little olive oil

FOR THE SALAD

- 250g | 8¾oz green beans, blanched
- 200g | 7oz baby courgettes, halved
- juice of 1 lemon
- 3tbsp extra virgin olive oil
- micro herbs or mustard and cress

INFORMATION
Per Serving

CALORIES
270

FAT
12g

SATURATED FAT
3g

CARBS
4g

METHOD

1 Put the chops into a bowl or ziplock bag. Stir together the beer and salt until dissolved. Pour over the pork, cover and leave overnight to marinate in the fridge.

2 When you are ready to cook, take the pork out of the brine and pat dry. Rub olive oil into the pork and grind over some black pepper. Cook for a few minutes on each side on a barbecue or griddle pan – timing will depend on the thickness of the meat.

3 To make the salad, mix together the beans, courgettes, lemon juice and olive oil with plenty of seasoning. Scatter over the micro herbs to serve.

Pesto Chicken Courgetti

This tried-and-tested combo is a midweek family meal winner

Serves 4 • Ready in 35 minutes

INGREDIENTS

- 750g | 1lb 10½oz courgettes
- olive oil spray
- 1tbsp olive oil
- 45g | 1½oz pine nuts
- 200g | 7oz mini chicken fillets
- 2tsp chicken seasoning
- 1 garlic clove, crushed
- 250g | 8¾oz tub quark
- small bunch of basil
- 400ml | 13½fl oz chicken stock

TIP

If you don't have a spiraliser you can use a julienne peeler or a mandoline to create courgetti

METHOD

1 Heat the oven to 200C | Gas 6 | 400F. Trim the courgettes, then use a spiraliser to create tagliatelle-style courgette ribbons. Spread the ribbons out onto one or two roasting tins and spritz with the olive oil spray. Cook in the oven for five minutes.

2 Heat the olive oil and fry the pine nuts for a few minutes, until golden brown. Set aside.

3 Add the chicken fillets, chicken seasoning and garlic to the pan. Fry for ten minutes, to lightly brown, turning as needed.

4 Put the quark, basil and chicken stock into a food processor and blitz to make a smooth liquid. Pour over the chicken and warm through. Toss together with the courgettes. Scatter with the pine nuts.

INFORMATION
Per Serving

CALORIES
257

FAT
12g

SATURATED FAT
1.5g

CARBS
6g

Chipotle Turkey Meatballs with Vegetable Spaghetti

High in protein, these meatballs really pack a flavour punch

Serves 4 • Ready in 45 mins

INGREDIENTS

- 500g | 1lb 1½oz turkey thigh mince
- 1tbsp Italian seasoning
- 1 onion, chopped
- 1 garlic clove, crushed
- 1tbsp olive oil
- 1 onion, chopped
- 1tbsp chipotle paste
- 400g | 14oz tomatoes
- small bunch basil leaves
- 500g | 1lb 1½oz mooli (white radish), peeled
- 500g | 1lb 1½oz courgettes, trimmed and washed

METHOD

1 Heat the oven to 200C | Gas 6 | 400F. Put the mince into a food processor with the Italian seasoning, onion and garlic. Season with salt and pepper, blend to combine, then shape into balls.

2 Line a roasting tin with a non-stick Teflon sheet, arrange the meatballs on top and cook in the oven for 25 minutes, turning as needed until lightly browned and cooked through.

3 For the sauce, heat the oil in a pan, add the onion and cook for a few minutes, to soften. Stir in the chipotle paste, tomatoes and several basil leaves. Gently simmer for five minutes.

4 Secure the vegetables in a spiraliser, and twist the handle to create long strands of mooli and courgettes. (Alternatively, carefully cut the vegetables into thin strips.) Spread out onto two lined baking trays and bake for just three minutes until warmed through.

5 Gently stir the vegetable spaghetti into the sauce. Season and mix with the meatballs and basil leaves.

INFORMATION
Per Serving

CALORIES
206

FAT
4g

SATURATED FAT
1.5g

CARBS
11g

COMPILED BY: JESSICA RANSOM. SALAD STYLING AND RECIPES: JESS FINDLAY AND JULES MERCER

Courgetti Puttanesca

The anchovies provide a health hit and give this dish that lovely salty tang

Serves 2 • Ready in 20 mins

INGREDIENTS

- 200g | 7oz passata
- 150g | 5¼oz cherry tomatoes, halved
- 2 garlic cloves, chopped
- 25g |¾oz (about 7) anchovies
- 2tsp capers, chopped
- 40g | 1½oz black olives
- 450g | 1lb (3-4) courgettes, spiralised or thinly sliced on a mandolin
- 2tsp toasted pine nuts
- few basil leaves, shredded, to serve

METHOD

1 Heat the passata in a small saucepan until it comes to a gentle simmer.

2 Reduce the heat and add the tomatoes, garlic, anchovies and capers with a generous grind of black pepper. Cook for five minutes, stirring to mash up the anchovies. Stir through the olives.

3 Blanch the courgettes until just tender – one to two minutes is fine. Drain and toss through the sauce. Serve topped with basil.

INFORMATION
Per Serving

CALORIES
170

FAT
7g

SATURATED FAT
1g

CARBS
11g

RECIPES: ROSE FOOKS AND JULES MERCER. PHOTOGRAPHS: JON ASHFORD. FOOD STYLING: LINDSAY HARRIS

Baked Cardamom and Pistachio Chicken Curry

There's nothing better than a prep-ahead, stick-in-the-oven dinner – and this clever recipe is just that

Serves 6 • Ready in 45 mins, plus marinating

INGREDIENTS

- 120g | 4¼oz smoked bacon lardons (optional)
- 4cm | 1½in piece of ginger, grated
- 2 garlic cloves, crushed
- 1 green chilli, deseeded and sliced
- 6 cardamom pods, seeds removed
- few drops of rose water
- 2tsp garam masala
- 2tsp ground turmeric
- 2tsp cornflour
- 500ml | 1pt natural yogurt
- 500g | 1lb 1½oz chicken breast, cut into chunks
- 1 onion, thinly sliced
- 1tsp olive oil
- 60g | 2oz pistachios, chopped

METHOD

1 In a large bowl, mix together the ginger, garlic, chilli, cardamom, rose water, garam masala, turmeric and cornflour. Stir through the yogurt, add the chicken (and lardons, if you're using them) and toss to coat. Leave to marinate in the fridge for at least four hours, or overnight if possible.

2 Heat the oven to 180C | Gas 4 | 350F. Toss the onion with the oil and a pinch of salt.

3 Tip the chicken and all the marinade into a baking dish. Scatter over the onion and pistachios. Bake for 25 to 30 minutes, until the chicken is cooked through. Scatter with dried rose

INFORMATION
Per Serving

CALORIES
221
FAT
9g

SATURATED FAT
2.5g

CARBS
9g

59

Mumbai Chicken Curry

This has a good kick from the chillies but is cooled down with the coconut sauce. The ingredients list might make this dish look a little bit daunting but much of it is the paste, which is simply whizzed up

Serves 6 • Ready in 1 hour 30 mins

INGREDIENTS

- 3tbsp olive oil
- 1¼kg | 2lb 12oz chicken thighs, boneless and skinless
- 4 tomatoes, finely chopped
- 400ml | 13½fl oz coconut cream
- 1tbsp tamarind paste
- a large bunch of fresh coriander, chopped

FOR THE PASTE

- 5 large red chillies, roughly chopped
- ½tsp ground cumin
- 1tsp ground coriander
- 6 peppercorns
- ½tsp cinnamon
- 5 cardamom pods, seeds removed
- 5cm | 2in piece ginger, peeled
- 5 garlic cloves, peeled
- 1 large onion, roughly chopped
- 2tsp garam masala

METHOD

1 Heat the oil in a large sauté pan and brown the chicken in batches; set aside. Whizz up all the paste ingredients in a food processor. Fry the paste in the sauté pan for a few minutes then add the chicken to the paste and coat well, stirring for a few minutes. Add the tomatoes, coconut cream and tamarind paste. Bring to the boil, then simmer, uncovered, for 50 minutes, until the chicken is tender.

2 You can freeze it at this point or it will keep in the fridge for two days. When you are ready to serve, stir in the fresh coriander. Serve with cauliflower rice, and a fresh tomato salad with a squeeze of lemon.

INFORMATION
Per Serving

CALORIES
415

FAT
19g

SATURATED FAT
13g

CARBS
11.5g

PHOTOGRAPHS: SEAN CALITZ. RECIPES AND FOOD STYLING: JANE CURRAN. PROP STYLING: SUE ROWLANDS

King Prawn Thai Red Curry

This impressive low-cal supper doesn't fail to deliver on flavour

Serves 4 • Ready in 25 mins

INGREDIENTS

- 3tbsp olive oil
- 3 garlic cloves, sliced
- 5cm | 2in piece of fresh ginger, peeled and sliced
- 2tsp paprika
- ½tsp chilli powder
- ½tsp Chinese five spice
- 5 spring onions, chopped
- 2 lemongrass stalks, split lengthways and bashed
- 1tbsp tomato ketchup
- 1 red pepper, sliced
- ½-1 red chilli, deseeded and sliced
- 450g | 1lb raw king prawn tails, peeled
- 3-4 kaffir lime leaves or zest of 1 lime
- 165ml | 5½ fl oz coconut milk
- 100g | 3½oz bean sprouts
- 1tbsp Thai fish sauce
- handful of Thai basil leaves (or other basil)

METHOD

1 Heat the oil in a wok and fry the garlic, ginger, spices and spring onions for one minute. Add the lemongrass, ketchup, red pepper, chilli and prawns, and stir-fry for two to three minutes.

2 Add the kaffir lime leaves and the coconut milk, lower the heat and simmer for five minutes.

3 Add the bean sprouts and simmer for one to two minutes. Take out the lemongrass. Add the fish sauce, scatter with basil leaves, and serve with cauliflower rice and lime halves.

COMPILED BY: TI MEDIA FOOD HUB. RECIPES AND PHOTOS: TI-MEDIACONTENT.COM

INFORMATION
Per Serving

CALORIES
261

FAT
16g

SATURATED FAT
7g

CARBS
7g

Tikka Grilled Paneer

This simple sweet dish is the perfect addition to your table, helping everyone up their veg count

Serves 4 • Ready in 10 mins

INGREDIENTS

- 250g | 8¾oz paneer, cut into cubes
- 2 peppers, diced
- 5tbsp tikka paste
- mint and coriander, chopped

METHOD

1 Mix the paneer and peppers with the tikka paste, spread over a baking tray and grill under a high heat for a few minutes, turning now and then, until softened and lightly charred. Serve with chopped mint, coriander and a side of cauliflower rice if you wish to eat it as a main.

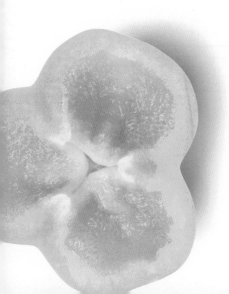

INFORMATION
Per Serving

CALORIES
290

FAT
22g

SATURATED FAT
11g

CARBS
8g

Crispy Sea Bass with Stir-Fried Veg

*Zingy Asian flavours jazz up this simple fish dish
and it looks really impressive on the table*

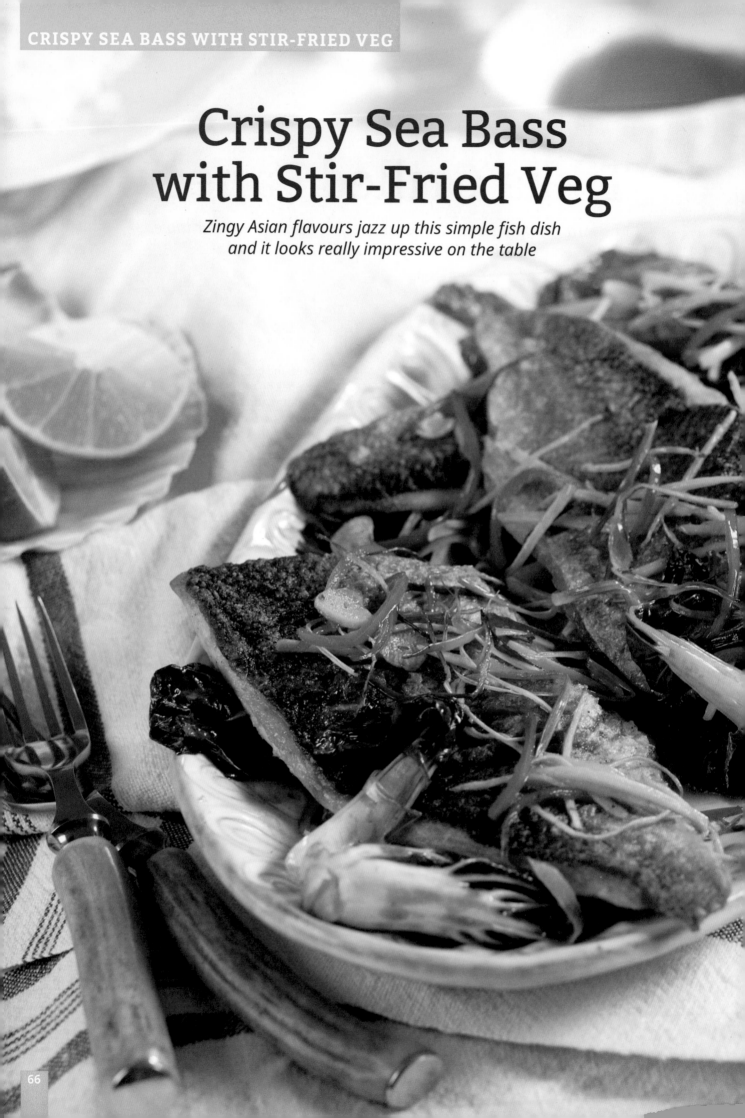

Serves 4 • Ready in 20 mins

INGREDIENTS

- 4 x 175g | 6¼oz sea bass fillets
- cornflour, to dust
- 2tsp groundnut oil
- 1tbsp toasted sesame oil
- 30g | 1oz root ginger, cut into matchsticks
- 1 red chilli, deseeded and cut into matchsticks
- bunch of spring onions, trimmed and shredded
- 3 garlic cloves, thinly sliced
- 400g | 14oz bok or pak choi, or choi sum
- 4tbsp teriyaki marinade
- lime wedges, to serve
- cauliflower rice, to serve

METHOD

1 Pat the fish dry with kitchen paper, then dust both sides with cornflour. Heat a splash of oil in a large frying pan, then drizzle the skin on each fillet with a little more oil and add to the pan, skin-side down. Cook for two to three minutes until the skin is crisp and golden. Turn and cook for a further minute.

2 Meanwhile, heat the sesame oil in a large wok, add the ginger, chilli and spring onions, and cook for two minutes over a high heat. Add the garlic and cook for a further minute, then spoon over the fish. Add the bok choi and teriyaki marinade immediately to the wok, cook over a high heat for a minute until wilted. Serve with the sea bass, lime wedges and cauliflower rice.

INFORMATION
Per Serving

CALORIES
344

FAT
20g

SATURATED FAT
4g

CARBS
6g

Duck and Mushroom Stir-Fry with Konjac Noodles

Transparent konjac noodles, made from an Asian plant, are now widely available in supermarkets and help make this a superb keto-friendly dish

Serves 2 • Ready in 15 mins

INGREDIENTS

- cooking spray
- 100g | 3½oz skinless duck steaks, thinly sliced
- 10g | ¼oz fresh root ginger, cut in matchsticks
- 1 garlic clove, thinly sliced
- 1 medium red chilli, thinly sliced
- 125g | 4½oz fresh shiitake mushrooms, sliced
- 2 spring onions, sliced
- 75g | 2½oz trimmed mangetout
- 200g | 7oz konjac noodles
- 3tbsp oyster sauce
- 1tbsp dark soy sauce
- 1tsp Thai fish sauce

METHOD

1 Spray a large frying pan or wok with oil, place over a medium heat and stir-fry the duck for three to four minutes to brown. Add the ginger, garlic and chilli, and stir-fry for a further minute.

2 Add the mushrooms and cook for two to three minutes until they begin to soften. Add the spring onions and mangetout and cook for a further minute.

3 Rinse the noodles under warm water, then add to the pan and toss to combine.

4 Mix the oyster, soy and fish sauces in a small bowl and pour into the stir-fry mix. Toss to coat well, then lower the heat and stir-fry for one to two minutes. Heap into warmed dishes and serve.

INFORMATION
Per Serving

CALORIES
125

FAT
4g

SATURATED FAT
1g

CARBS
8g

COMPILED BY ROSE FOOKS. PHOTOS TI-MEDIACONTENT.COM

Herby Olive and Tomato Roast Chicken

A meltingly tender fuss-free roast that even makes its own 'instant gravy'

Serves 6 • Ready in 1 hour 30 mins

INGREDIENTS

- 2kg | 4lb 6½oz free-range chicken
- 2 lemons, halved
- 100g | 3½oz pitted black olives
- 300g | 10½oz small tomatoes, quartered
- 200g | 7oz shallots, peeled
- 6 sprigs thyme, leaves only from half
- 12 garlic cloves, unpeeled
- 3tbsp olive oil
- handful flat-leaf parsley, chopped

METHOD

1 Heat the oven to 200C | Gas 6 | 400F. Sit the chicken, breast-side down in a roasting tin. Season well and squeeze the juice of half a lemon over the skin and insides of the chicken.

2 In a bowl, mix together the olives, tomatoes, shallots, thyme, garlic, 2tbsp of the oil, juice of one lemon and the parsley. Season generously with freshly ground black pepper.

3 Spoon half the mixture inside the chicken, along with the remaining half of lemon, then spoon the rest around the chicken. Season and drizzle with the remaining oil.

4 Roast for 20 minutes, then turn the chicken over and baste well. Reduce the oven to 180C | Gas 4 | 350F and roast for a further 50 minutes to one hour until cooked. Rest for ten minutes then carve and serve with the tomatoey olive juices.

INFORMATION
Per Serving

CALORIES
506

FAT
18g

SATURATED FAT
3g

CARBS
6g

RECIPES AND STYLING: ELISA ROCHE, SAMUEL GOLDSMITH, ROSE FOOKS, JESSICA RANSOM AND KEIRON GEORGE. PHOTOS: SAM STOWELL. PROPS: SUE ROWLANDS

Roast Side of Salmon with Blushing Veg

This mouthwatering salmon is so easy to prepare and will make a delightful, impressive centrepiece at your table

Serves 8 • Ready in 40 mins

INGREDIENTS

- 450g | 1lb mixed radishes
- 250g | 8¾oz asparagus tips
- 300g | 10½oz baby leeks
- 3tbsp olive oil
- zest of 1 lemon
- 1kg | 2lb 3¼oz side salmon, skin on

FOR THE DRESSING

- 1 banana shallot, finely chopped
- large bunch of fresh herbs (we used parsley, dill and lemon thyme)
- 50g | 1¾oz olive oil
- juice of 1 lemon
- 1tsp cracked pink peppercorns, to garnish

METHOD

1 Heat the oven to 200C | Gas 6 | 400F . Place the radishes, asparagus and baby leeks on a large baking tray, and drizzle with 2tbsp of the oil, and season with salt and pepper. Toss everything together with the lemon zest to coat the vegetables evenly.

2 On a separate baking tray lined with parchment, place the salmon on top, skin-side down, and brush with the remaining olive oil. Season well.

3 Place both trays in the oven for 25 minutes, until the salmon is just cooked through and the vegetables are nicely roasted. Serve hot or at room temperature with the dressing.

4 For the dressing, simply blitz all the ingredients together, and drizzle over the salmon and vegetables.

INFORMATION
Per Serving

CALORIES
420

FAT
26g

SATURATED FAT
6g

CARBS
2.6g

Chipotle Braised Beef

Serve the meat in the pot, or on a platter with the sauce to spoon over at the table – you choose

Serves 6 • Ready in 3 hours 20 mins, plus marinating

INGREDIENTS

- 1kg | 2lb 3¼oz beef sirloin or brisket
- 27g | 1oz sachet chipotle rub
- 3tbsp olive oil
- 2 banana shallots, chopped
- 2 garlic cloves, crushed
- 2tsp ground coriander
- 2tsp ground cumin
- 1 ancho chilli, rehydrated and chopped
- 1 chipotle chilli, rehydrated and chopped
- 1 cascabel chilli, rehydrated and chopped
- 400g | 14oz passata
- 150ml | 5fl oz red wine
- 1tbsp red wine vinegar
- 500ml | 1pt beef stock
- 2tsp dried oregano
- juice of 1 orange
- red onion, avocado and tomato

METHOD

1 Put the beef in a dish and coat all over with the chipotle rub. Cover, and leave to marinate in the fridge for at least two hours.

2 Heat 1tbsp of the oil in a casserole. Brown the beef then remove from the pan. Add the remaining oil and fry the shallots, garlic, spices and chillies until they are aromatic.

3 Return the beef to the casserole, add the remaining ingredients and cook, covered, for two to three hours on a very low heat, until really tender.

4 Remove the meat from the pot and reduce the sauce to a thick, syrupy consistency. Carve the beef and then return it to the pot or serve on a platter. Garnish with onion, avocado and tomato.

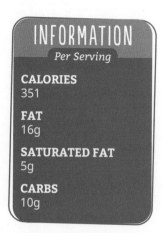

INFORMATION
Per Serving

CALORIES
351

FAT
16g

SATURATED FAT
5g

CARBS
10g

Summer Ratatouille

Fresh tomatoes and generous quantities of fragrant herbs makes this ratatouille vibrant and tasty

Serves 4 • Ready in 40 mins

INGREDIENTS

- 3 red peppers, roughly chopped
- 2 onions, roughly chopped
- 1 small fennel bulb, roughly chopped
- 3tbsp olive oil
- 2 courgettes, roughly chopped
- few sprigs of fresh thyme
- 3 garlic cloves, thinly sliced
- 125g | 4½oz black olives
- 270g | 9½oz cherry tomatoes, quartered
- handful of flat-leaf parsley and basil leaves
- small head of celery, roughly chopped

METHOD

1 Heat the oven to 180C | Gas 4 | 350F. Toss the celery, red peppers, onions and fennel in 2tbsp olive oil on a baking tray. Roast for ten minutes, until just soft. Add the courgettes and thyme, tossing to coat in the olive oil, and roast for another ten minutes. Remove from the oven and set aside.

2 Heat the remaining 1tbsp olive oil in a large frying pan over a medium heat. Fry the garlic until just golden. Add the roasted vegetables, olives and cherry tomatoes. Cook over a medium heat for a further few minutes, until the tomatoes are warmed through but still holding their shape. Remove from the heat, scatter with the parsley and basil, and serve.

INFORMATION
Per Serving

CALORIES
200

FAT
14g

SATURATED FAT
2g

CARBS
11g

Mussels With Dry Sherry, Garlic and Thyme

This starter with sherry, garlic and thyme is a smart way to kick off a dinner party – buy the mussels on the day of cooking

Serves 6 • Ready in 25 mins

INGREDIENTS

- 75g | 2¾oz butter
- 1 large onion, finely chopped
- 2 garlic cloves, finely chopped
- 250ml | 8½fl oz dry sherry (we used Fino)
- 1tbsp fresh thyme leaves
- 3kg | 6lb 9¾oz mussels, cleaned and de-bearded

METHOD

1 Melt the butter in a large saucepan with a lid and add the onion and garlic. Cook gently without colouring for around five to ten minutes, until the onion has softened.

2 Turn up the heat and add the sherry and thyme leaves. Bubble until the raw alcohol smell wears off, then tip in the mussels, cover the pan tightly and cook, shaking every so often, for around five minutes, until the mussels have opened. Discard any that remain tightly closed.

3 Check the seasoning of the sauce and serve immediately.

INFORMATION
Per Serving

CALORIES
273

FAT
14g

SATURATED FAT
7g

CARBS
2.5g

Ginger and Lemongrass Salmon

Salmon's rich taste works so well with South-East Asian spices

Serves 8 to 10 • Ready in 40 mins, plus marinating

INGREDIENTS

- 2 lemongrass stalks, tough outer layer removed, stalks bashed and finely chopped
- 4 x 5cm | 2in pieces root ginger, peeled and sliced
- 3tbsp soy sauce
- 1tbsp Thai fish sauce
- 1tbsp rice vinegar
- 1tbsp sweet chilli sauce
- 1 whole side of salmon
- handful chopped fresh coriander
- lime wedges
- teriyaki sauce

METHOD

1 Combine the lemongrass, ginger, soy sauce, fish sauce, rice vinegar and sweet chilli sauce in a bowl, stir and pour over the salmon, encased in foil to form a boat. Marinate in the fridge for at least two hours or overnight if you are preparing ahead.

2 Heat the oven to 220C | Gas 7 | 425F. Bake the salmon in the centre of the oven for 20 to 25 minutes until it is cooked through but not too flaky. Scatter with the fresh coriander and serve immediately with the lime wedges and the teriyaki sauce to spoon over it, or allow the salmon to cool to room temperature before garnishing.

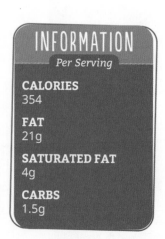

INFORMATION
Per Serving

CALORIES
354

FAT
21g

SATURATED FAT
4g

CARBS
1.5g

Duck and Healthy Greens Salad

Think Chinese-style crispy duck with a punchy Asian dressing and crunchy greens – a lighter version of a rich weekend meal

Serves 6 • Ready in 2 hours 45 mins

INGREDIENTS

- 4 duck legs
- 150ml | 5fl oz soy sauce
- 7½cm | 3in piece of root ginger, roughly chopped
- 4 garlic cloves, bruised
- 2 star anise
- 1 cinnamon stick

FOR THE SALAD

- 300g | 10½oz Tenderstem broccoli
- 300g | 10½oz kale, shredded
- 4tbsp mixed seeds, lightly toasted

FOR THE DRESSING

- 2tbsp sweet miso paste
- 1tbsp toasted sesame oil
- juice of 2 limes

METHOD

1 Put the duck skin side down in a deep pan and pour over the soy sauce and enough water to cover. Add the ginger, garlic, star anise and cinnamon, cover with a lid and bring to the boil. Reduce the heat to a simmer and cook for 30 minutes. Turn the duck legs over and continue poaching for 1-1½ hours or until tender. Remove from the heat and set aside to cool, then remove from the cooking liquor and pat dry.

2 Meanwhile, bring a pan of water to the boil, cook the broccoli for two minutes then rinse in cold water and set aside. Put the kale in a large bowl, cover with boiling water and leave for a minute. Drain, rinse under cold water, and then set aside.

3 Heat the oven to 200C | Gas 6 | 400F. Put the duck in the oven, skin side up, for 20 to 30 minutes, until crisp. Shred while hot. Combine the dressing ingredients until smooth, then toss with the kale, broccoli, shredded duck and seeds. It will keep for four hours.

INFORMATION
Per Serving

CALORIES
294

FAT
15g

SATURATED FAT
3g

CARBS
11g

Prawn Cocktail Parcels

These can be assembled a couple of hours before serving, and garnished just before taking to the table

Serves 4 • Ready in 20 mins

INGREDIENTS

- 200g | 7oz smoked salmon slices
- 150g | 5¼oz cooked tiger prawns
- 1 ready-to-eat avocado, peeled and cut into cubes
- 5 heaped tbsp mayonnaise
- 3tbsp tomato ketchup or chutney
- 2tsp Worcestershire sauce
- splash of Tabasco sauce
- juice of 1 lemon
- 1tsp paprika
- micro salad leaves, to serve

METHOD

1 Line ramekins with the smoked salmon, allowing an overhang, as you'll need to fold this over the bases once filled.

2 For the Marie Rose sauce, mix together the mayonnaise, ketchup, Worcestershire sauce and Tabasco sauce. Season to taste with lemon juice and salt and pepper. Reserve four tiger prawns for decorating the tops. Mix the remaining prawns, along with the avocado, into the sauce and use to fill each of the lined ramekins. Fold the overhang of smoked salmon over the top and place in the fridge until ready to serve.

3 To serve, turn out the prawn cocktail parcels carefully onto serving plates and garnish with the salad leaves. Place a whole tiger prawn on top and finish with a sprinkling of paprika.

RECIPES AND FOOD STYLING: ELISA ROCHE. ROSE FOOKS, JESSICA RANSOM AND KEIRON MURPHY. PHOTOGRAPHS: SEAN CALITZ. PROP STYLING: SUE ROWLANDS

INFORMATION
Per Serving

CALORIES
344

FAT
27g

SATURATED FAT
4g

CARBS
5g

Pesto Pork with Sautéed Cabbage & Leek

This quick leafy dish is ideal for a night in for two

Serves 2
Ready in 15 mins

INGREDIENTS

- 200g | 7oz trimmed lean pork medallions
- olive oil cooking spray
- 1tsp olive oil
- 400g | 14oz shredded cabbage and leek mix
- 4tsp pesto
- lemon wedge

METHOD

1 Season the pork medallions with salt and pepper. Spray a small frying pan with the oil and cook the pork medallions over a medium heat for three to four minutes each side, until just cooked through and nicely golden.

2 Meanwhile, heat the olive oil in a medium-sized frying pan and cook the cabbage and leek mix over a medium heat for five to six minutes, stirring occasionally until it's just tender.

3 Season generously, then spoon onto warmed plates. Top with the pork, spoon over the pesto and serve with a wedge of lemon.

INFORMATION
Per Serving

CALORIES
266

FAT
10g

SATURATED FAT
3g

CARBS
7g

Flank Steak with Hot Salsa Verde

This juicy steak board, inspired by Brazilian barbecues, is hard to resist. We served ours with padron peppers

Serves 6 • Ready in 30 mins

INGREDIENTS

- 750g | 1lb 10½oz beef skirt steak, fillet or hanger

FOR THE SALSA VERDE

- ½ bunch flat-leaf parsley
- ½ bunch basil, leaves picked
- ½ bunch mint, leaves picked
- 1tbsp red wine vinegar
- 5 drops Tabasco
- 100ml | 3½fl oz extra virgin olive oil, plus 1tbsp extra for the meat
- 45g | 1½oz anchovies
- 1tsp Dijon mustard

FOR THE TOPPING

- 45g | 1½oz small capers
- 1 spring onion, chopped
- 1 red chilli, sliced and deseeded
- 1 green pepper, sliced

METHOD

1 Bring the meat to room temperature and pat down with olive oil, salt and pepper. Set aside. Meanwhile, heat a griddle pan or barbecue, until smoking with dry heat.

2 While the barbecue heats up, make the salsa verde. Place all the salsa ingredients in a small food processor, season to taste and whizz to a rough, oily paste.

3 Now place the steak on the grill and cook for three to four minutes a side for medium-rare. Rest, lightly covered with foil, for five minutes.

4 Serve sliced on a board, doused in salsa verde and topped with capers, spring onions, chilli and green pepper.

INFORMATION
Per Serving

CALORIES
340

FAT
26g

SATURATED FAT
5.6g

CARBS
2g

RECIPES AND STYLING: ELISA ROCHE. ROSE FOOKS, JESSICA RANSOM, KEIRON GEORGE. PHOTOS: GEORGIA GLYNN SMITH. PROP STYLING: JANE BERRY

Chinese Spiced Pork Belly with Plums

This dish is a good way to make the most of tasty, but great-value, pork

Serves 8 • Ready in 6 hrs 30 mins

INGREDIENTS

- 1¼kg | 2lb 12¾oz pork belly, cut into slices
- 2 cinnamon sticks
- 3 star anise
- 1tsp Chinese five spice
- 6 plums, halved
- 150ml | 5fl oz red wine
- juice of 2 oranges
- 1 chicken stock pot
- 150g | 5¼oz Chinese greens, such as pak choi or tatsoi

METHOD

1 Put the pork into a slow cooker with the cinnamon, star anise, five spice, plums, wine, orange juice and stock pot. Cook on low for six hours or high for three hours. Alternatively, put the ingredients into a casserole with a scrunched-up piece of wet greaseproof paper inside the lid and cook in the oven on its lowest setting for four to six hours.

2 Skim off the fat, add the Chinese greens so that the stalks are immersed and allow to steam for two to three minutes. Serve with mixed vegetables or cauliflower rice.

COMPILED BY: T1 MEDIA FOOD HUB CONTENT AND PHOTOS: T1MEDIACONTENT.COM

INFORMATION
Per Serving

CALORIES
860

FAT
66g

SATURATED FAT
23g

CARBS
10g

Devilled Eggs with Crab

Using a mix of brown and white crab meat in this fancy twist on the buffet classic, gives the best result

Serves 12 • Ready in 25 mins

INGREDIENTS

- 12 large eggs
- 60g | 2oz good-quality mayonnaise
- 1 garlic clove, crushed
- 1tsp mustard powder
- juice of 1 lemon, and a little zest
- 1tsp Tabasco sauce (optional)
- 400g | 14oz mixed crab meat
- a few sprigs of fresh dill, to serve

METHOD

1 Bring a large pan of water to the boil. Reduce to a simmer, add the eggs and cook for seven minutes. Transfer the eggs to a large bowl of cold water; leave for ten minutes then peel the eggs and discard the shells.

2 Cut each egg in half and scoop out the yolk, putting them into a large bowl. Use a fork to mash together the yolks, mayo, garlic, mustard powder, lemon juice and zest, and crab meat. Season the mix.

3 Spoon the mixture back into the egg whites and serve topped with the dill.

INFORMATION
Per Serving

CALORIES
76

FAT
5g

SATURATED FAT
1g

CARBS
0g

RECIPES AND FOOD STYLING ROSE FOOKS, JULES MERCER, JESS FINDLAY. PHOTOS: SEAN CALITZ. PROPS: SUE ROWLANDS

Fisherman's Sea Bream with Aioli

You can also use sea bass for this recipe. The aioli makes more than you need but keeps for five days in the fridge and is delicious served with other meals, too

Serves 2 • Ready in 40 mins

INGREDIENTS

- 1 small bulb fennel, chopped
- 150g | 5¼oz brown cap mushrooms, thickly sliced
- 200g | 7oz small tomatoes, halved
- pinch of saffron threads
- 150ml | 5fl oz dry white wine
- few sprigs of fresh thyme
- 1 sea bream, 750g to 850g | 1lb 10½oz to 1lb 14oz, scaled and gutted
- 5 fresh bay leaves

FOR THE MARINADE

- 3 garlic cloves, crushed
- juice of 1 lemon
- 2 egg yolks
- 275ml | 9¼fl oz olive oil

METHOD

1 Start by making the aioli. Mix together the garlic, lemon and egg yolks with pinch of salt. Gradually whisk in the oil and keep whisking (an electric hand mixer is best for this part) until thickened. Check the seasoning – you may want to add more salt or lemon. Set aside, covered in the fridge.

2 Heat the oven to 220C | Gas 7 | 425F. Gently warm the olive oil in a sauté pan and cook the fennel for ten minutes until slightly softened. Add the mushrooms and cook for a few minutes. Put into a shallow roasting tin and add the tomatoes, saffron, white wine and thyme. Season well. Stuff the cavity of the sea bream with the bay leaves.

3 Put the bream on top of the tomato mixture then bake in the oven for about 15 minutes or until the fish is cooked through. Serve with the aioli on the side.

INFORMATION
Per Serving

CALORIES
676

FAT
35g

SATURATED FAT
3.5g

CARBS
5g

Chicken with Chorizo

Who doesn't love a one-pan dish? This meal bursts with all the flavours of summer and has a lovely smoky aroma from the chorizo

Serves 2 • Ready in 1 hour and 15 mins

INGREDIENTS

- 8 pieces of chicken – thighs, breast or drumsticks
- 4tbsp olive oil
- 200g | 7oz cooking chorizo, cut into chunks
- 1 aubergine, cut into chunks
- 1 red pepper, cut into chunks
- 1 bunch of kale, stalks removed and leaves chopped
- 400g | 14oz chopped tomatoes
- 1 bunch of oregano
- handful of olives (optional)
- 50g | 2¾oz feta, crumbled

METHOD

1 Preheat the oven to 200C | Gas 6 | 400F. Place the chicken in an ovenproof dish and toss together with the olive oil, chorizo, aubergine and red pepper. Roast for 30 minutes until the vegetables are just charred and the chicken is coloured.

2 Remove the dish from the oven, add the kale and tinned tomatoes, and stir in the oregano. Return to the oven for a further 25 minutes until the sauce has thickened and the chicken is cooked through. Remove from the oven and add the olives, if you're using them. Top with feta and serve.

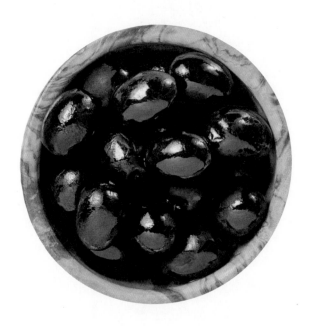

INFORMATION
Per Serving

CALORIES
705

FAT
40g

SATURATED FAT
12g

CARBS
9g

Spring Pork and Cider Casserole

*A quick one-pot with zesty, punchy flavours.
Serve with a crunchy salad*

Serves 4 • Ready in 35 mins

INGREDIENTS

- 1tbsp olive oil
- 600g | 1lb 5oz pork loin fillet, sliced into medallions
- 1 red onion, thinly sliced
- 2 garlic cloves, grated
- 2tsp fennel seeds
- 500ml | 1pt low-carb cider
- 3tbsp crème fraîche
- 75g | 2½oz mixed pitted olives
- 3tbsp capers
- zest and juice of 2 lemons
- a large handful of parsley, chopped

METHOD

1 Heat the oil in a heavy-based casserole and fry the pork in batches for two minutes on each side, until browned and almost cooked through. Set aside.

2 Gently cook the onion with the garlic and fennel seeds until the onion has softened. Turn up the heat, pour over the cider and boil until reduced by half. Return the pork to the pan for five minutes, until just cooked through.

3 Stir through the crème fraîche, olives, capers, lemon zest and juice. Season and scatter with parsley to serve.

INFORMATION
Per Serving

CALORIES
362

FAT
18g

SATURATED FAT
6g

CARBS
6g

Middle East-Inspired Lamb

An easy recipe for anyone with leftover spices in the cupboard, this cooks slowly and melts in the mouth

Serves 8 • Ready in 1 hour 30 mins

INGREDIENTS

- 2tbsp olive oil
- 2 large onions, sliced
- 2 garlic cloves, sliced
- 5cm | 2in piece fresh root ginger, grated
- 2tsp ground cinnamon
- 2tsp ground cumin
- 1tsp paprika
- 2tsp ras-el-hanout blend
- 1kg | 2lb 3¼oz lean leg lamb, cut into chunks
- 250ml | 8½fl oz chicken stock
- 12-18 fresh figs (or dried)
- 45g | 1½oz chopped pistachios
- 6tbsp chopped fresh coriander and mint
- pomegranate seeds, to serve (optional)

METHOD

1 In a large casserole dish, heat half the oil and cook the onions for ten minutes. Add the garlic, ginger and all the spices. Stir well and cook for two to three minutes. Add the lamb and mix it well into the spices, stirring. Add the chicken stock and some seasoning, then bring to the boil and simmer for one hour or until the lamb is tender. At this point, you can cool then put it in the fridge for up to two days, or freeze.

2 When you're ready to serve, heat the oven to 200C | Gas 6 | 400F. Halve the figs and put cut-side-up in a lined dish. Drizzle over the remaining oil, and roast for ten minutes. Add to the lamb and stir in gently. Scatter over the pistachios, herbs and pomegranate seeds, if you are using them.

INFORMATION
Per Serving

CALORIES
598

FAT
25g

SATURATED FAT
9g

CARBS
11.5g

Tomato, Chicken and Olive Stew

This warm Mediterranean stew makes for a great family meal

Serves 6 • Ready in 40 mins

INGREDIENTS

- 4 skinless chicken breasts
- 4tsp stock powder
- 2tbsp olive oil
- 1 red onion, chopped
- 2 carrots, finely chopped (optional)
- 2 garlic cloves, sliced
- 2tbsp tomato purée
- 1kg | 2lbs 3¼oz fresh plum tomatoes
- 20g | ¾oz pack basil, shredded, reserving a few leaves for the garnish
- 1tbsp capers
- 2tbsp sliced olives

METHOD

1 Put the chicken breasts in a pan with the stock powder and pour over 1 litre | 2 pints of boiling water. Simmer for 25 minutes, or until the chicken is cooked through.

2 Meanwhile, heat the oil in another large pan, or casserole, and gently cook the onion and carrots for ten minutes. Add the garlic and tomato purée and stir into the veg. Cook for a further two minutes.

3 Put the tomatoes and the basil into a food processor and whizz, then add to the pan with the veg. Cook for 20 minutes, until reduced and the sauce has thickened.

4 Break up the chicken and add to the tomato sauce, with a little chicken stock, as needed. Garnish with basil. Serve scattered with the capers and olives.

INFORMATION
Per Serving

CALORIES
213
FAT
7g
SATURATED FAT
11g
CARBS
9g

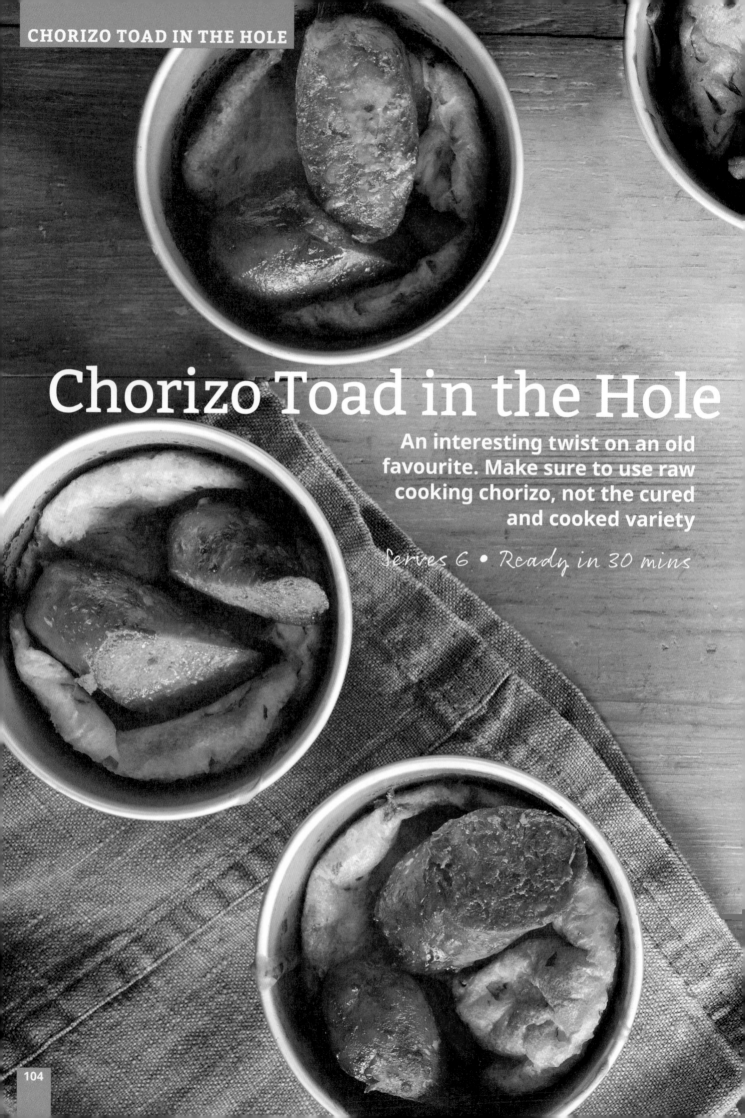

Chorizo Toad in the Hole

An interesting twist on an old favourite. Make sure to use raw cooking chorizo, not the cured and cooked variety

Serves 6 • Ready in 30 mins

INGREDIENTS

- 6 mini (10cm | 4in) Yorkshire pudding tins
- 6 raw chorizo
- 75g | 2¾oz plain flour
- 1 free-range egg
- 125ml | 4¼fl oz semi-skimmed milk
- 2tbsp chopped flat-leaf parsley
- 3tbsp oil

METHOD

1 Grill or fry the chorizo until lightly browned. Heat the oven to 200C | Gas 7 | 400F. Sift the flour into a large bowl, season and make a well in the centre. Break in the egg and beat with an electric whisk then whisk in the milk. Stir through the parsley.

2 Divide the oil between the tins and heat through in the oven. Halve the chorizo and put two halves in each tin. Divide the batter between the tins and bake for around 15 minutes until risen and well browned.

INFORMATION
Per Serving

CALORIES
270

FAT
19g

SATURATED FAT
1g

CARBS
12g

Grilled Courgette and Ricotta Bake

Even die-hard meat lovers will adore this delicious bake

Serves 4 to 6 • Ready in 1 hour 15 mins

INGREDIENTS

- a shallow ovenproof gratin dish
- 1kg | 2lb 3¼oz courgettes, trimmed and thickly sliced lengthways
- 5tbsp olive oil
- sea salt
- 3 leeks, sliced
- 120g | 4¼oz baby kale, blanched and excess water squeezed out
- 500g | 1lb 1½oz ricotta
- 3 egg yolks
- 75g | 2¾oz Parmesan
- 100ml | 3½fl oz double cream

METHOD

1 First, grill the courgettes. Toss in 4tbsp olive oil with plenty of salt and pepper then put under a hot grill (you will probably need to do this in two batches) until well browned on one side. Set aside.

2 Cook the leeks in the remaining oil until tender. Set aside. Mix together the kale, ricotta, egg yolks, Parmesan (reserve 2tbsp) and double cream.

3 To assemble, put the leeks in the base of the dish, cover with a layer of courgettes, then the ricotta mixture and finally the remaining courgettes to cover the top. Heat the oven to 180C | Gas 4 | 350F. Sprinkle over the remaining Parmesan and bake for 50 minutes until browned and bubbling. Serve with a green salad. This also makes a great side dish to serve eight with roast chicken or grilled fish.

INFORMATION
Per Serving

CALORIES
656

FAT
53g

SATURATED FAT
24g

CARBS
12g

Black Bean Frittata

Layers of black beans, halloumi and olives form a delicious meal

Serves 6 • Ready in 35 mins

INGREDIENTS

- 1tbsp olive oil
- 1 green pepper, roughly chopped
- 1 red pepper, roughly chopped
- 4 spring onions, sliced
- 1 garlic clove, minced
- 1 red chilli, deseeded and sliced
- 1 can black beans, drained and rinsed
- 6 eggs
- 30g | 1oz finely chopped coriander
- 150g | 5¼oz halloumi, sliced
- 100g | 3½oz kalamata olives, pitted
- soured cream and salsa, to serve

METHOD

1 Heat the oven to 180C | Gas 4 | 350F. Heat the oil in a 26cm | 10in non-stick ovenproof pan. Add the peppers and onions, and cook for four minutes. Add the garlic and chilli, and cook for a further minute, then stir through the beans.

2 Meanwhile, beat the eggs with 2tbsp water, add the coriander and season. Add the egg mixture to the pan and cook for five minutes, gently lifting up the edges with a spatula to allow any uncooked egg mixture to distribute evenly.

3 Lay the halloumi and olives on top and transfer the pan over to the oven. Bake for 15 to 20 minutes, until golden.

4 Cut into wedges and serve with a dollop of soured cream and salsa.

INFORMATION
Per Serving

CALORIES
282

FAT
18g

SATURATED FAT
6.5g

CARBS
11g

Courgette and Tomato Gratin

This delicious bake is perfect if you're entertaining vegetarians

Serves 4 • Ready in 45 mins

INGREDIENTS

- 1 red pepper
- 6 tomatoes
- 2tbsp olive oil
- 1 red onion, finely sliced
- 2 garlic cloves, crushed
- 1tbsp mint, chopped
- 1tbsp basil, chopped
- 1tbsp parsley, chopped
- 1-2 medium courgettes
- 50g | 1¾oz cheddar cheese, grated

METHOD

1 Cut the red pepper in half and discard the core. Dice the pepper and two tomatoes. Heat 1tbsp oil in a pan and fry the sliced onion, crushed garlic and diced pepper until tender. Add the chopped tomato and most of the herbs, then cook for five minutes until softened.

2 Spoon half this mixture into a shallow gratin/baking dish. Heat the oven to 180C | Gas 4 | 350F.

3 Slice the courgettes and the remaining tomatoes and toss into the gratin/baking dish. Sprinkle over seasoning and add the remaining pepper mixture, then drizzle with the remaining oil.

4 Bake for 20 minutes until the vegetables are almost tender, then sprinkle with the cheese and the rest of the herbs. Cook for a further five minutes until the cheese has melted.

INFORMATION
Per Serving

CALORIES
139

FAT
12g

SATURATED FAT
3.5g

CARBS
9.5g

Spinach, Olive and Feta Oven Frittata

Leftover frittata is perfect for a packed lunch

Serves 6 • Ready in 40 mins

INGREDIENTS

- sandwich tin, buttered and lined with baking parchment
- 1tbsp light olive oil
- 1 red onion, sliced
- 80g | 2¾oz bag baby spinach
- 200g | 7oz pack feta cheese, roughly cubed
- 50g | 1¾oz pitted black olives, halved
- 6 large eggs, beaten

METHOD

1 Heat the oven to 180C | Gas 4 | 350F. Heat the oil in a frying pan, add the onion and cook over a medium heat for five to seven minutes. Turn off the heat and add the spinach until it wilts. Spoon into the lined tin.

2 Add the feta and olives and stir to mix up slightly. Season the beaten eggs well with salt and pepper and then pour over the vegetables.

3 Bake in the oven for 20 to 25 minutes, or until it's just set in the centre. Remove from the oven and leave to cool in the tin for a few minutes, then transfer to a wire rack to cool completely. Cut into wedges to serve.

INFORMATION
Per Serving

CALORIES
224

FAT
18g

SATURATED FAT
7g

CARBS
9.2g

INFORMATION
Per Serving

CALORIES
262

FAT
21g

SATURATED FAT
9.5g

CARBS
4g

Spiced Baked Ricotta

Ricotta is high in protein, and rich in vitamins A and D, plus calcium

Serves 4
Ready in 45 mins

INGREDIENTS

- 4tsp each fennel seeds, coriander seeds and cumin seeds
- 1tsp sea salt
- 2 x 250g | 8¾oz ricotta cheese
- 2tbsp olive oil
- 200g | 7oz mixed tomatoes, larger ones halved

METHOD

1 Put the spices into a small frying pan and heat gently until they release their aromas. Roughly grind with a mortar and pestle. Add the salt and some freshly ground black pepper then spread out onto a small plate.

2 Drain the ricotta of any liquid. Heat the oven to 180C | Gas 4 | 350F. Line a baking tray with oiled foil. Roll the sides and top the ricotta in the spices then transfer with a fish slice to the baking tray. Drizzle over 1tbsp of the oil and bake for 25 minutes.

3 To serve, put the tomatoes into a frying pan with the remaining oil and sea salt and pepper. Toss until warmed through and serve with the ricotta, halved.

Berry Frozen Yogurt

This easy dessert is so quick to put together and works well as a treat

Serves 8 • Ready in 10 mins plus freezing

INGREDIENTS

- 1 can coconut cream
- 375ml | 12¾fl oz coconut milk yogurt
- 3tbsp icing sugar or sweetener
- 300g/10½oz mixed frozen berries

METHOD

1 Whisk the coconut cream, yogurt and icing sugar together until smooth. Stir in the berries and crush slightly. Turn into a container and freeze until firm, preferably overnight.

2 Allow to soften at room temperature for half an hour before serving.

INFORMATION
Per Serving

CALORIES
150

FAT
13g

SATURATED FAT
11g

CARBS
8.5g

No-churn Fresh Raspberry Ice Cream

Good for a reward from time to time or pleasing friends and family, this makes enough for ten to 12 servings

Serves 12 • Ready in 1hr, plus freezing

INGREDIENTS

- 250g | 8¾oz fresh raspberries, plus extra to serve
- juice of 1 lemon
- 180ml | 6fl oz heavy cream
- 50g | 1¾oz sweetener, like Swerve
- 15g | ½oz butter
- 600ml | 1¼pt double cream
- 2tsp vanilla extract

METHOD

1 To make the purée, put the raspberries and lemon juice in a pan and heat gently until they are mushy. Push through a sieve to remove pips and leave to cool.

2 Create a keto condensed milk by combining the heavy cream, sweetener and butter into a pan. Simmer for about half an hour until reduced to a thick consistency. Leave to cool.

3 Whisk the condensed milk, cream and vanilla together then stir in the raspberry purée. Pour into a freezer-proof lidded box for eight hours before serving. To serve, leave at room temperature for around 45 minutes then scoop into glasses. Top with some fresh raspberries.

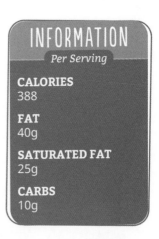

INFORMATION
Per Serving

CALORIES
388

FAT
40g

SATURATED FAT
25g

CARBS
10g

Piña Colada Panna Cotta

Bring a little sunshine to the table. If you like piña coladas, you'll love these tropical puddings

Serves 4 • Ready in 20 mins, plus setting

INGREDIENTS

- 4 dariole moulds or ramekins
- 3 gelatine leaves
- 200g | 7oz coconut yogurt
- 1tbsp coconut rum
- 1 mango
- 4 thin wedges of pineapple, skin left on (optional)
- 1tbsp toasted coconut flakes

METHOD

1 Bring 100ml | 3½fl oz water to the boil. Add the gelatine and whisk to dissolve.

2 In a bowl, mix the yogurt and rum together and keep stirring while slowly pouring in the gelatine mix. Pour 75ml | 3fl oz of the mix into each mould and set in the fridge for three hours.

3 Peel the mango (discard the skin), then use a peeler to shave the flesh into ribbons.

4 If you're using them, grill the pineapple wedges in a pan over a medium heat for two minutes on each side until golden.

5 Dip the set panna cotta pots into warm water and unmould onto plates. Serve with the pineapple and mango, and scattered with coconut flakes.

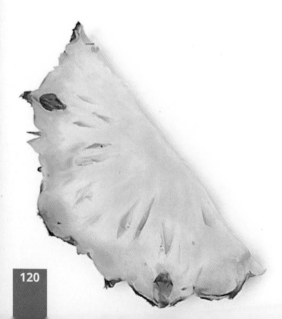

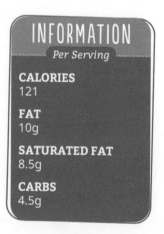

INFORMATION
Per Serving

CALORIES
121

FAT
10g

SATURATED FAT
8.5g

CARBS
4.5g

Chocolate Mousse with Nut Medley

Enjoyed responsibly, this dish is an indulgent once-in-a-while treat

INGREDIENTS

- 165g | 5¾oz keto-friendly dark chocolate, like Lilly's or Choc Zero
- 6 large free-range eggs, yolks separated
- 1tbsp of water, coffee or liqueur
- 1tbsp sweetener
- 200g | 7oz mixed toasted nuts, blanched hazelnuts and pecans

METHOD

1 Melt the chocolate and leave it to cool. Put the egg yolks in a bowl, gently beat to loosen, then pour in the chocolate and 1tbsp water.

2 Very gently fold together using a balloon whisk. Using an electric whisk, mix the egg whites and sweetener until the mixture is stiffly peaking. Fold a quarter into the chocolate mix, then the rest.

3 Divide between eight jars or bowls and leave to set in the fridge for at least two hours. Scatter with the nuts once ready to serve.

Serves 8 • Ready in 50 mins, plus setting

INFORMATION
Per Serving

CALORIES
485

FAT
23g

SATURATED FAT
7g

CARBS
12g

Chocolate Truffles

These rich, bite-size crowd-pleasers are ideal for gatherings, and can be enjoyed with an after-dinner coffee

Serves 30 to 40 • Ready in 30 mins, plus setting

INGREDIENTS

- 300ml | 10fl oz whipping cream
- pinch of salt
- 300g | 10oz keto-friendly dark chocolate, broken into pieces
- 50g | 1¾oz unsalted butter, softened
- few drops of vanilla extract
- 2-3tbsp cocoa

METHOD

1 Bring the cream and salt to the boil and pour it over the chocolate. Stir the chocolate until melted, then add the butter and vanilla. Mix very well to give a smooth mixture – using a stick blender will speed up this stage. Chill the mixture until just set.

2 Shape the mixture into balls, either with a melon baller or by scooping out with a teaspoon and rolling between your hands. If it's soft, chill until firmer.

3 Roll the truffles in cocoa, shaking off any excess, and leave in a cool place – but not the fridge – to set. Once set, they will keep in the fridge for a week.

INFORMATION
Per Serving

CALORIES
54

FAT
5.5g

SATURATED FAT
3.5g

CARBS
0.5g

Peanut Butter Fudge

*These chunky squares of buttery,
sweet fudge are packed with protein*

Serves 21 • Ready in 30 mins, plus freezing

INGREDIENTS

- 200g | 7oz desiccated coconut
- 225g | 8oz peanut butter
- 110ml | 3¾fl oz coconut oil, melted
- 3-5tbsp sugar-free syrup
- pinch of sea salt
- 1tsp vanilla extract
- handful of peanuts, to decorate
- 50g | 1¾oz dark chocolate, melted,
  to decorate (optional)

METHOD

1 Add the desiccated coconut to a food processor and blend until a creamy paste is formed.

2 Add the peanut butter and coconut oil, and blitz before adding the syrup one spoon at a time. Make sure to taste the mixture so the preferred level of sweetness is reached.

3 Finally, add the sea salt and vanilla. Transfer the mixture to a baking tray and spread until even.

4 Place in the freezer until firm (around 15 minutes). Drizzle with melted dark chocolate, if you're using it, and scatter with peanuts. Then use a hot knife to slice into even squares and serve at room temperature.

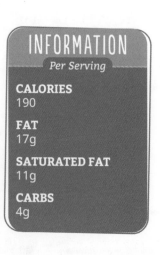

INFORMATION
Per Serving

CALORIES
190

FAT
17g

SATURATED FAT
11g

CARBS
4g

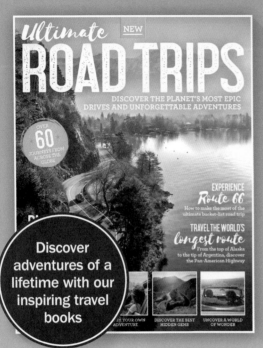
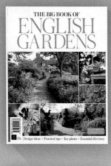

 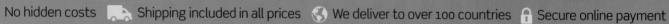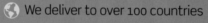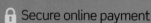